HORMONE RESET DIET

REBALANCE THEM HORMONES!

Proven Ways To Return Balance To Your Hormone Levels To Increase Weight Loss and Metabolism For Better Energy and Vitality

SARAH BERRY

from the Publisher. All additional right reserved.

Table of Contents

PART I 11

Hormone Diet 12

Chapter 1: Health Benefits of the Hormone Diet 12

Chapter 2: Hormone-Rebalancing Smoothies 15

    Estrogen Detox Smoothie 15

    Dopamine Delight Smoothie 17

    Breakfast Smoothie Bowl...18

    Blueberry Detox Smoothie...20

    Maca Mango Smoothie 21

    Pituitary Relief Smoothie 22

Chapter 2: Easy Breakfast Recipes 23

    Scrambled Eggs With Feta and Tomatoes......................................23

    Smashed Avo and Quinoa 25

    Hormone Balancing Granola 27

Chapter 3: Healthy Lunch Recipes 29

    Easy Shakshuka...29

    Ginger Chicken...31

    Carrot and Miso Soup...33

    Arugula Salad..35

    Kale Soup 37

    Roasted Sardines 38

Chapter 4: Tasty Dinner Recipes...40

    Rosemary Chicken...41

    Corned Beef and Cabbage...43

Roasted Parsnips and Carrots 44

Herbed Salmon 45

Chipotle Cauliflower Tacos 47

PART II 49

Chapter 1: How to Reset Your Body? 50

Chapter 2: Science Behind Metabolism Reset 52

Chapter 3: Recipes for Smoothies and Salads 54

Green Smoothie 54

Strawberry Banana Smoothie 55

Salmon Citrus Salad 56

Chapter 4: Quick and Easy Breakfast and Main Course Recipes 58

Quinoa Salad 58

Herb and Goat Cheese Omelet 60

Mediterranean Cod 62

Grilled Chicken and Veggies 64

Stuffed Peppers 67

Brussels Sprouts With Honey Mustard Chicken 70

Quinoa Stuffed Chicken 72

Kale and Sweet Potato Frittata 74

Walnut, Ginger, and Pineapple Oatmeal 75

One-Pot Chicken Soup 78

Chocolate Pomegranate Truffles 80

PART III 81

Chapter 1: Easy Recipes for Managing Kidney Problems 82

Pumpkin Pancakes 83

Pasta Salad 84

Broccoli and Apple Salad 85

Pineapple Frangelico Sorbet...87

Egg Muffins..88

Linguine With Broccoli, Chickpeas, and Ricotta................90

Ground Beef Soup 93

Apple Oatmeal Crisp 94

Chapter 2: Weekend Recipes for Renal Diet 95

Hawaiian Chicken Salad Sandwich......................................95

Apple Puffs...96

Creamy Orzo and Vegetables...98

Minestrone Soup 100

Frosted Grapes 102

Yogurt and Fruit Salad...103

Beet and Apple Juice Blend..105

Baked Turkey Spring Rolls..106

Crab-Stuffed Celery Logs..108

Couscous Salad 109

Chapter 3: One-Week Meal Plan 111

Chapter 4: Avoiding Dialysis and Taking the Right Supplements 113

PART IV 117

Chapter 1: Causes and Symptoms of Hashimoto Disease......................118

Chapter 2: Recipes for Appetizers and Snacks......................123

Oven Roasted Okra..123

Honeydew Smoothie Bowl..125

Wake-Up Smoothie 126

Cucumber Radish Salsa..127

Crispy Oven-Fried Fish Tacos..128

Strawberry Mango Salsa 131

Grilled Salmon and Veggies 133

Chapter 3: Main Course Recipes 135

Zucchini Noodles With Shrimp and Avocado Pesto 135

Honey Ginger Shrimp Bowls...137

Beef and Sweet Potatoes Stew 140

Roasted Sunchoke Salad...142

Kale Salad 143

Taco Spaghetti Squash Boats...145

Lemon Asparagus Chicken Skillet...147

Egg Roll in a Bowl 149

One-pan Chicken Pesto 151

BBQ Jackfruit 153

Chapter 4: How to Increase Immunity to Prevent Further Relapse? 155

PART V...157

Chapter 1: Tasty Breakfast Options..158

French Crepe 158

Chapter 2: Delicious Salads 162

Traditional French Country Salad With Lemon Dijon Vinaigrette...........162

Chapter 3: Soup..164

Classic French Onion Bistro Soup 164

Fresh French Pea Soup 166

Green Vegetable Soup..168

Chapter 4: Beef Options 170

Beef Bourguignon - Slow-Cooked 170

Entrecote Steak With Red Wine Sauce....................................173

Pan-Seared Steak au Poivre 175

Steak Diane 177

Chapter 5: Other Delicious French Classics 179

French Ham & Grilled Cheese Sandwich - Croque Monsieur 179

Pork Chops With Mustard Sauce 181

Provencal Chicken Casserole 183

White Wine Coq Au Vin..184

PART V 186

Grilling Rub 187

Chapter 1: Seafood..189

Lemony Shrimp & Tomatoes 189

Sea Bass With Garlic Butter 191

Chapter 2: Pork..193

Grilled Sausages With Summer Veggies..193

Honey-Chipotle Ribs..195

Peachy Pork Ribs...197

Pork Loin Steaks 199

Chapter 3: Poultry...201

Chicago-Style Turkey Dogs 201

Dr. Pepper Drumsticks 202

Grilled Lemon Chicken 203

Ground Turkey Burgers 205

Spiced Chicken With Cilantro Lime Butter 207

Turkey Pepper Kabobs 209

Chapter 4: Beef..210

Classic Beef Cheeseburgers...211

Grilled Skirt Steak With Peppers & Onions...................................213

Tangy Lime Top Round Steak...215

Whiskey Cheddar Burgers...216

Chapter 5: Dessert 218

Grilled Pineapple With Lime Dip 218

Take Care Of Your Grill! 219

PART I

Hormone Diet

Are you worried that your hormones are not at their optimal levels? Here is a diet that will solve your problems.

Chapter 1: Health Benefits of the Hormone Diet

When it comes to getting healthy through weight loss, there's never any shortage of fitness crazes and diets that claim to have the secret to easy and sustainable weight loss. One of the latest diet plans that have come into the spotlight is the hormone diet, which claims that people often struggle to lose weight because of their hormones.

A hormone diet is a 3-step process that spans over six weeks and is designed to synchronize your hormones and promote a healthy body through detoxification, nutritional supplements, exercise, and diet. The diet controls what you eat and informs you about the correct time to eat to ensure maximum benefits to your hormones. Many books have been written on this topic with supporters of the diet assuring people that they can lose weight quickly and significantly through diet and exercise and reset or manipulate their hormones. Although the diet has a few variations, the central idea around each is that correcting the body's perceived hormonal imbalances is the key to losing weight.

The most important benefit of a hormone diet is that it takes a solid stance on improving overall health through weight loss and promoting regular exercise as well as natural, nutritious foods. Apart from that, it also focuses on adequate sleep, stress management, emotional health, and other healthy lifestyle habits that are all essential components that people should follow, whether it's a part of a diet or not. Including a water diet, it aims towards losing about twelve pounds in the 1st phase and 2 pounds a week after that.

Hormones have an essential role in the body's everyday processes, like helping bones grow, digesting food, etc. They act as "chemical messengers," instructing the cells to perform specific actions and are transported around the body through the bloodstream.

One of the very important food items to be included in the hormone diet is salmon. Salmon is rich in omega-3 fatty acids, Docosahexaenoic acid, and Eicosapentaenoic acid (EPA). It is rich in selenium too. These help to lower your blood pressure and also reduce the level of unhealthy cholesterol in the blood. These make you less prone to heart diseases. Salmon is a rich source of healthy fat. If consumed in sufficient amounts, it provides you energy and helps you get rid of unwanted body fat. Salmon is well-known for giving fantastic weight loss results as it has less saturated fat, unlike other protein sources. Salmon is packed with vitamins like vitamin-k, E, D, and A. These are extremely helpful for your eyes, bone joints, etc. These vitamins are also good for your brain, regulation of metabolic balance, and repairing your muscles. Salmon's vitamins and omega-3 fatty acids are amazing for sharpening your mind. It also improves your memory retention power. If you consume salmon, you are less likely to develop dementia or mental dis-functions. Salmon has anti-inflammatory properties and is low in omega-6 fatty acid content (which is pro-inflammatory in nature and is present in a huge amount in the modern diet). It promotes healthy skin and gives you radiant and glowing skin. It is good for the winter because it helps you to stay warm. It also provides lubrication to your joints because of the abundant presence of essential minerals and fatty acids in it. Apart from this, some other things to include in your diet are arugula, kale, ginger, avocado, carrots, and so on.

There are almost sixteen hormones that can influence weight. For example, the hormone leptin produced by your fat cells is considered a "satiety hormone," which makes you feel full by reducing your appetite. As a signaling hormone, it communicates with the part of your brain (hypothalamus) that controls food intake and appetite. Leptin informs the brain when there is enough fat in storage, and extra fat is not required. This helps prevent overeating. Individuals who are obese or overweight generally have very high levels of leptin in their blood. Research shows that the level of leptin in obese individuals was almost four times higher than that in individuals with normal weight.

Studies have found that fat hormones like leptin and adiponectin can promote long-term weight loss by reducing appetite and increasing metabolism. It is believed that both these fat hormones follow the same pathway in the brain to manage blood sugar (glucose) and body weight (Robert V. Considine, 1996).

Simply put, the hormone diet works by helping to create a calorie deficit through better nutritional habits and exercise, which ultimately results in weight loss. It's also essential to consult a doctor before following this detox diet or consuming any dietary supplements.

Chapter 2: Hormone-Rebalancing Smoothies

Estrogen Detox Smoothie

Total Prep & Cooking Time: 5 minutes

Yields: One glass

Nutrition Facts: Calories: 312 | Carbs: 47.9g | Protein: 18.6g | Fat: 8.5g | Fiber: 3g

Ingredients:

- Half a cup of hemp seeds
- Two kiwis (medium-sized)
- A quarter each of
  - Avocado (medium-sized)
  - Cucumber (medium-sized)
- Half a unit each of
  - Lemon (squeezed freshly)
  - Green apple
- One celery (medium-sized)
- A quarter cup of cilantro
- Two tbsps. of chis seeds
- Two cups of water (filtered)
- One tsp. of cacao nibs
- One tbsp. of coconut oil

Method:

1. Blend the ingredients all together to form a smoothie at high speed. The thickness can be adjusted according to your preference by adding more water to the mixture.

2. Serve and enjoy.

Dopamine Delight Smoothie

Total Prep Time: 10 minutes

Yields: One serving

Nutrition Facts: Calories: 383 | Carbs: 31g | Protein: 24g | Fat: 18.g | Fiber: 3g

Ingredients:

- Half a teaspoon of cinnamon (ground)
- Half a cup of peeled banana (the bananas must be frozen)
- One organic espresso, double shot (measuring half a cup)
- One tablespoon of chia seeds
- A three-fourth cup of soy milk (plain or vanilla-flavored)
- Protein powder, a serving (from the whey with the flavor of vanilla)

Method:

1. Fill in the bowl of your blender with all the ingredients (from the section of ingredients) except the whey protein powder and then proceed by switching to a high-speed blending option. Make sure it acquires a smooth consistency and then pour it out.

2. Now you may add the protein powder and give it another shot of blend until the whole things get incorporated, a bit of the goat cheese (already crumbled).

Breakfast Smoothie Bowl

Total Prep Time: 10 minutes

Yields: 2 servings

Nutrition Facts: Calories: 290 | Carbs: 53g | Protein: 6g | Fat: 8g | Fiber: 9g

Ingredients:

- One cup of thoroughly rinsed blueberries (fresh and ripe)
- A sundry of nuts and fruits for garnishing, which includes – strawberries, bananas (thinly sliced), peanuts (Spanish), kiwi (chopped), segments of tangerine, and raspberries.
- One cup of Greek yogurt

For the preparation of honey flax granola,

- Two tablespoons each of
  - Flaxseeds
  - Vegetable oil
- Oats (old-fashioned), approximately a cup
- One tablespoon of honey

Method:

1. Set your oven at a temperature of 350 degrees F.

2. Preparation of the smoothie: collect the diverse types of berries, wash them thoroughly, and then put them in the blender and turn it on. Make an even mixture out of it. Add some amount of the yogurt and blend it again to form a smooth texture.

3. For preparing the granola: Take a small-sized bowl and then drizzle a few drops oil in it. Then add the oats, flax, and honey to the oil, one by one, and mix it well. You are required to toss the bowl thoroughly to get the mixture well-coated with the poured oil. After you are done, place the oats mixture in a baking sheet evenly. Bake it for about twenty minutes. This mark will be enough to give the oats a beautiful tinge of golden brown. Allow it to cool.

4. Now you will require a shallow bowl to spoon in some yogurt, and this will be the first layer. Form a second layer with the various fruits and nuts and finally for the third layer, top with the granola.

5. Enjoy.

Notes:

- *Using frozen nuts and fruits in a warm-weather will get much to your relief.*

- *For a vegan smoothie bowl, sub the yogurt with coconut or almond yogurt.*

- *Give the pan a few strokes while baking the oats.*

Blueberry Detox Smoothie

Total Prep Time: Ten minutes

Yields: One serving

Nutrition Facts: Calories: 326 | Carbs: 65g | Protein: 4g | Fat: 8g | Fiber: 9g

Ingredients:

- One cup of wild blueberries (frozen)
- One banana (sliced into several pieces) frozen
- Orange juice (approximately half a cup)
- Cilantro leaves, fresh (approximately a measuring a small handful size)
- A quarter of an entire avocado
- A quarter cup of water

Method:

1. Add cilantro, avocado, water, blueberries, banana, and orange juice in the blender and then process.

2. Make the ingredients integrated so well that they become smooth in their consistency.

Notes: *It is recommended that you add the potent herb, cilantro, or parsley in a small amount when consuming this smoothie for the first time, as it might trigger a mild headache. If you do not get a headache, you may add a bit more of the cilantro leaves.*

Maca Mango Smoothie

Total Prep & Cooking Time: 2 minutes

Yields: 2 servings

Nutrition Facts: Calories: 53 | Carbs: 13g | Protein: 1g | Fat: 3g | Fiber: 1.5g

Ingredients:

- One and a half cups each of
  - Fresh mango
  - Frozen mango
- One tablespoon each of
  - Ground flaxseed
  - Nut butter
- One teaspoon of ground turmeric
- Two teaspoons of maca root powder
- Three-quarter cups of nut milk
- One frozen banana

Method:

1. Blend all the ingredients together to get a smooth mixture.

2. Adjust consistency by adding nut milk.

3. Once done, divide into two glasses and enjoy!

Pituitary Relief Smoothie

Total Prep & Cooking Time: 5 minutes

Yields: 2 servings

Nutrition Facts: Calories: 174 | Carbs: 18.3g | Protein: 9.7g | Fat: 8.3g | Fiber: 14.4g

Ingredients:

- One teaspoon of coconut oil
- One fresh or frozen ripe banana
- One tablespoon of raw sesame seeds
- Two teaspoons each of
  - Chia seeds
  - Raw Maca powder
  - Raw Spirulina
- Two cups of water
- Two tablespoons of hulled hemp seeds

Method:

1. You have to use a blender to process this smoothie. Add the hulled hemp seeds, sesame seeds, and water in the blender and process them. Do it at high speed, and it will only require a minute. This will give you raw-milk like texture.

2. Then, add the following ingredients into it – coconut oil, banana, chia seeds, Maca, and Spirulina, and process the ingredients once again but this time on medium speed for another minute or so. Everything will become well incorporated.

3. You have to drink this smoothie on an empty stomach.

Notes: *In order to make the smoothie rich in antioxidants, you can add some fresh fruits like blueberries, kiwi, and raspberries.*

Chapter 2: Easy Breakfast Recipes

Scrambled Eggs With Feta and Tomatoes

Total Prep & Cooking Time: 10 minutes

Yields: One Plate

Nutrition Facts: Calories: 421 | Carbs: 8.6g | Protein: 20.3g | Fat: 35.1g | Fiber: 1.6g

Ingredients:

- One tbsp. each of
    o Olive oil (extra virgin)
    o Freshly chopped parsley, basil, dill or chives
- Half a cup of cherry tomatoes (each tomato sliced into half)
- Two ounces of crumbled feta cheese (approximately a quarter cup)
- Two eggs are beaten
- Two tbsp. of onion (diced)
- To taste:
    o Black pepper
    o Kosher salt

Method:

1. Keep the beaten eggs in a small-sized bowl and then season it with a pinch of pepper and salt. Set the bowl aside.

2. Use a nonstick skillet to proceed with the cooking. Pour two tbsp. of olive oil. Then add the diced onions. Stir over moderate heat and cook until softened. Make sure that the onions do not look brown. This process should get done by a minute.

3. Add half a cup of tomatoes to skillet and then continue to mix for about two minutes.

4. Now you may add the eggs. Using a spatula, gather the beaten eggs to the center by moving spatula all over the skillet.

5. The eggs will take an additional minute to get cooked. So after that mark, add the parsley or other herbs (if preferred) and feta cheese. Keep the eggs underdone as they will get cooked completely after they are served in the plate itself (from the residual heat). Therefore, cook the entire thing in the skillet for 30 seconds only.

6. Take a serving plate and transfer the eggs to it. Top with some sprinkled parsley and feta cheese, drizzled with some oil, and seasoned with some pepper and salt. These additions are optional and may vary as per your desire.

Smashed Avo and Quinoa

Total Prep & Cooking Time: 15 minutes

Yields: Six bowls

Nutrition Facts: Calories: 492 | Carbs: 67g | Protein: 15g | Fat: 20g | Fiber: 13g

Ingredients:

- One avocado skinned, cut into half, and then pitted
- A handful of cilantro or coriander
- Half a lemon (juiced)
- A quarter red onion (diced finely)
- One-eighth teaspoon of cayenne pepper
- To taste: Sea salt

For the Greens,

- One handful of kale
- One handful of soft herbs (basil, parsley or mint)
- One handful of chard or spinach
- For frying: butter or coconut oil

Serve with,

- One cup of quinoa (cooked)

Method:

1. You will require a frying pan to get this done. To it, add the coconut oil or butter (whichever you prefer) and add the greens. Toss them carefully and then sauté over moderate heat. Stop when they become soft.

2. Mix the onion, cayenne, avocado, cilantro, salt, lemon, and pepper to a bowl and mix them completely. The pepper and salt must be added according to the taste.

3. Add cooked quinoa to the tossed greens and heat altogether over low heat.

4. Take a serving plate and place the quinoa mixture and greens to it. Crown the whole thing with smashed avocado and then serve.

Hormone Balancing Granola

Total Prep & Cooking Time: 35 minutes

Yields: 8 servings

Nutrition Facts: Calories: 360 | Carbs: 19.8g | Protein: 5.1g | Fat: 28.8g | Fiber: 5.8g

Ingredients:

- One-third cup each of
  - Flaxseed meal
  - Pumpkin seeds
  - Seedless raisins
- Two teaspoons of cinnamon
- One teaspoon of vanilla extract
- Four tablespoons of maple syrup
- Five tablespoons of melted coconut oil
- A quarter cup of unsweetened coconut flakes
- Two-thirds cup each of
  - Chopped pecans
  - Chopped brazil nuts
- Two tablespoons of ground chia seeds

Method:

1. Set the temperature of the oven to 180 degrees F and preheat.

2. In a food processor, chop the pecans and the Brazil nuts. Then, mix these chopped nuts with coconut flakes, seeds, and other nuts present in the list of ingredients.

3. Add maple syrup, coconut oil, cinnamon, and vanilla extract in a separate bowl and combine well.

4. Now, take the wet ingredients and pour them into the dry ingredients. Mix thoroughly so that everything has become coated properly.

5. Place the prepared mixture in the oven for half an hour and cook.

6. Once done, cut into pieces and serve.

Chapter 3: Healthy Lunch Recipes

Easy Shakshuka

Total Prep & Cooking Time: 30 minutes

Yields: Six servings

Nutrition Facts: Calories: 154 | Carbs: 4.1g | Protein: 9g | Fat: 7.8g | Fiber: 0g

Ingredients:

- Olive oil (extra virgin)
- Two chopped green peppers
- One teaspoon each of
  - Paprika (sweet)
  - Coriander (ground)
- A pinch of red pepper (flakes)
- Half a cup of tomato sauce
- A quarter cup each of
  - Mint leaves (freshly chopped)
  - Parsley leaves (chopped freshly)
- One yellow onion, large-sized (chopped)
- Two cloves of garlic, chopped
- Half a teaspoon of cumin (ground)
- Six cups of chopped tomatoes (Vine-ripe)
- Six large-sized eggs

- To taste: Pepper and salt

Method:

1. You will require a large-sized skillet (made of cast iron). Pour three tablespoons of oil and heat it. After bringing the oil to boil, add the peppers, spices, onions, garlic, pepper, and salt. Stir time to time to cook the veggies for five minutes until they become softened.

2. After the vegetables become soft, add the chopped tomatoes and then tomato sauce. Cover the skillet and simmer for an additional fifteen minutes.

3. Now, you may remove the lid from the pan and then cook a touch more to thicken the consistency. At this point, you may adjust the taste.

4. Make six cavities within the tomato mixture and crack one egg each inside the cavities.

5. Cover the skillet after reducing the heat and allow it to cook so that the eggs settle into the cavities.

6. Keep track of the time and accordingly uncover the skillet and then add mint and parsley. Season with more black and red pepper according to your desire. Serve them warm with the sort of bread you wish.

Ginger Chicken

Total Prep & Cooking Time: 50 minutes

Yields: Six Servings

Nutrition Facts: Calories: 310 | Carbs: 6g | Protein: 37g | Fat: 16g | Fiber: 1g

Ingredients:

- A one-kilogram pack of chicken thighs (skinless and boneless)
- Four cloves of garlic (chopped finely)
- A fifteen-gram pack of coriander (fresh and chopped)
- Two tablespoons of sunflower oil
- One teaspoon each of
  - Turmeric (ground)
  - Chili powder (mild)
- A four hundred milliliter can of coconut milk (reduced-fat)
- One cube of chicken stock
- One ginger properly peeled and chopped finely (it should be of the size of a thumb)
- One lime, juiced
- Two medium-sized onions
- One red chili, sliced and the seeds removed (fresh)

Method:

1. Make the chicken thighs into three large chunks and marinate them with chili powder, garlic, coriander (half of the entire amount), ginger, oil (one tbsp.), and lime juice. Cover the bowl after stirring them well and then store it in the fridge until oven-ready.

2. Marinade the chicken and keep overnight for better flavor.

3. Chop the onions finely (it is going to be the simplest for preparing the curry) before dropping them into the food processor. Pour oil into the frying pan (large-sized) and heat it. Then add chopped onions and stir them thoroughly for eight minutes until the pieces become soft. Then pour the turmeric powder and stir for an additional minute.

4. Now add the chicken mixture and cook on high heat until you notice a change in its color. Pour the chicken stock, chili, and coconut milk and after covering the pan simmer for another twenty minutes. Sprinkle the left-over coriander leaves and then serve hot.

5. Enjoy.

Carrot and Miso Soup

Total Prep & Cooking Time: 1 hour

Yields: Four bowls of soup

Nutrition Facts: Calories: 76 | Carbs: 8.76g | Protein: 4.83g | Fat: 2.44g | Fiber: 1.5g

Ingredients:

- Two tbsps. of oil
- Garlic, minced (four cloves)
- One inch of garlic (grated)
- Three tbsps. of miso paste (white)
- One diced onion
- One pound of carrot (sliced thinly)
- Four cups of vegetable stock
- To taste: Pepper and Salt

For garnishing,

- Two scallions (sliced thinly)
- Chili pepper (seven spices)
- One nori roasted (make thin slivers)
- Sesame oil

Method:

1. Using a soup pot will be convenient to proceed with. Pour oil in a pot and then heat over a high flame. Now you may put garlic, carrot, and onion and sauté them thoroughly. Cook for about ten minutes so that the onions turn translucent.

2. Then add the ginger and vegetable stock. Mix them well and cook all together. Put the flame to simmer. Cover the pot while cooking to make the carrot tender. This will take another thirty minutes.

3. Put off the flame and puree the soup with the help of an immersion blender.

4. Use a small-sized bowl to whisk together a spoonful of the soup and the white miso paste. Stir until the paste dissolve and pour the mixture back to the pot.

5. Add pepper and salt if required.

6. Divide the soup among four bowls and enrich its feel by adding scallions, sesame oil, seven spices, and nori.

Arugula Salad

Total Prep & Cooking Time: 1 hour 10 minutes

Yields: Two bowls of salad

Nutrition Facts: Calories: 336.8 | Carbs: 30.6g | Protein: 7.7g | Fat: 22.2g | Fiber: 7.3g

Ingredients:

For the salad,

- Two medium-sized beets (boiled or roasted for about an hour), skinned and sliced into pieces that can easily be bitten
- Four tablespoons of goat cheese
- Approximately 2.5 oz. of baby arugula (fresh)
- A quarter cup of walnuts (chopped roughly before toasting)

For the dressing,

- Three tablespoons of olive oil (extra virgin)
- A quarter tsp. each of
  o Mustard powder (dried)
  o Pepper
- Half a tsp. each of
  o Salt
  o Sugar

- One and a half tablespoons of lemon juice

Method:

1. For preparing the vinaigrette, place all the ingredients (listed in the dressing ingredients section) in a jar and then shake them to emulsify. At this stage, before starting with the process of emulsification, you may add or remove the ingredients as per your liking.

2. Get the salad assembled (again depending upon the taste you want to give it), add a fistful of arugula leaves, place some chopped beets (after they have been cooked), and finally the toasted walnuts (already chopped).

3. Drizzle vinaigrette over the salad and enjoy.

Notes:

- *Coat the beets with oil (olive), roll them up in an aluminum foil, and then roast the beets at a temperature of 400 degrees F.*

- *And for boiling the beets, immerse them in water after transferring to a pot and simmer them for 45 minutes.*

Kale Soup

Total Prep & Cooking Time: 55 minutes

Yields: 8 servings

Nutrition Facts: Calories: 277.3 | Carbs: 50.9g | Protein: 9.6g | Fat: 4.5g | Fiber: 10.3g

Ingredients:

- Two tbsps. of dried parsley
- One tbsp. of Italian seasoning
- Salt and pepper
- Thirty oz. of drained cannellini beans
- Six peeled and cubed white potatoes
- Fifteen ounces of diced tomatoes
- Six vegetable Bouillon cubes
- Eight cups of water
- One bunch of kale (with chopped leaves and stems removed)
- Two tbsps. of chopped garlic
- One chopped yellow onion
- Two tbsps. of olive oil

Method:

1. At first, take a large soup pot, add in some olive oil, and heat it.

2. Add garlic and onion. Cook them until soft.

3. Then stir in the kale and cook for about two minutes, until wilted.

4. Pour the water and add the beans, potatoes, tomatoes, vegetable bouillon, parsley, and the Italian seasoning.

5. On medium heat, simmer the soup for about twenty-five minutes, until the potatoes are cooked through.

6. Finally, do the seasoning with salt and pepper according to your taste.

Roasted Sardines

Total Prep & Cooking Time: 25 minutes

Yields: 4 servings

Nutrition Facts: Calories: 418 | Carbs: 2.6g | Protein: 41g | Fat: 27.2g | Fiber: 0.8g

Ingredients:

- 3.5 oz. of cherry tomatoes (cut them in halves)
- One medium-sized red onion (chopped finely)
- Two tablespoons each of
  o Chopped parsley
  o Extra-virgin olive oil
- One clove of garlic (halved)
- Eight units of fresh sardines (gutted and cleaned, heads should be cleaned)
- A quarter teaspoon of chili flakes
- One teaspoon of toasted cumin seeds
- Half a lemon (zested and juiced)

Method:

1. Set the temperature of the oven to 180 degrees C and preheat. Take a roasting tray and grease it lightly.

2. Take a bowl and add the tomatoes and onions in it. Add the lemon juice too and toss the veggies in the lemon juice. Now, add the zest, olive oil, chili, cumin, garlic, and parsley and toss everything once again.

3. Use pepper and salt to season the mixture. The cavity of the sardines has to be filled. Use some of the tomato and onion mixture for this purpose. Once done, place the sardines on the prepared roasting tray. Take the remaining mixture and scatter it over the sardines.

4. Roast the sardines for about 10-15 minutes, and by the end of this, they should be cooked thoroughly.

5. Serve and enjoy!

Chapter 4: Tasty Dinner Recipes

Rosemary Chicken

Total Prep & Cooking Time: 50 minutes

Yields: 4 servings

Nutrition Facts: Calories: 232 | Carbs: 3.9g | Protein: 26.7g | Fat: 11.6g | Fiber: 0.3g

Ingredients:

- Four chicken breast halves (skinless and boneless)

- One-eighth tsp. kosher salt

- One-fourth tsp. ground black pepper

- One and a half tbsps. of lemon juice

- One and a half tbsps. of Dijon mustard

- Two tbsps. of freshly minced rosemary

- Three tbsps. of olive oil

- Eight minced garlic cloves

Method:

1. At first, preheat a grill to medium-high heat. The grate needs to be lightly oiled.

2. Take a bowl and add lemon juice, mustard, rosemary, olive oil, garlic, salt, and ground black pepper. Whisk them together.

3. Take a resealable plastic bag and place the chicken breasts in it. Over the chicken, pour the garlic mixture (reserve one-eighth cup of it).

4. Seal the bag and start massaging the marinade gently into the chicken. Allow it to stand for about thirty minutes at room temperature.

5. Then on the preheated grill, place the chicken and cook for about four minutes.

6. Flip the chicken and baste it with the marinade reserved and then cook for about five minutes, until thoroughly cooked.

Finally, cover it with a foil and allow it to rest for about 2 minutes before you serve them.

Corned Beef and Cabbage

Total Prep & Cooking Time: 2 hours 35 minutes

Yields: 5 servings

Nutrition Facts: Calories: 868.8 | Carbs: 75.8g | Protein: 50.2g | Fat: 41.5g | Fiber: 14g

Ingredients:

- One big cabbage head (cut it into small wedges)
- Five peeled carrots (chopped into three-inch pieces)
- Ten red potatoes (small)
- Three pounds of corned beef brisket (along with the packet of spice)

Method:

1. At first, in a Dutch oven or a large pot, place the corned beef, and cover it with water. Then add in the spices from the packet of spices that came along with the beef. Cover the pot, bring it to a boil, and finally reduce it to a simmer. Allow it to simmer for about 2 hours and 30 minutes or until tender.

2. Add carrots and whole potatoes, and cook them until the vegetables are tender. Add the cabbage wedges and cook for another fifteen minutes. Then finally remove the meat and allow it to rest for fifteen minutes.

3. Take a bowl, place the vegetables in it, and cover it. Add broth (which is reserved in the pot) as much as you want. Then finally cut the meat against the grain.

Roasted Parsnips and Carrots

Total Prep & Cooking Time: 1 hour

Yields: 4 servings

Nutrition Facts: Calories: 112 | Carbs: 27g | Protein: 2g | Fat: 1g | Fiber: 7g

Ingredients:

- Two tbsps. of freshly minced parsley or dill
- One and a half tsp. of freshly ground black pepper
- One tbsp. kosher salt
- Three tbsps. of olive oil
- One pound of unpeeled carrots
- Two pounds of peeled parsnips

Method:

1. At first, preheat your oven to 425 degrees.

2. If the carrots and parsnips are thick, then cut them into halves lengthwise.

3. Then, slice each of them diagonally into one inch thick slices. Don't cut them too small because the vegetables will anyway shrink while you cook them.

4. Take a sheet pan, and place the cut vegetables on it.

5. Then add some olive oil, pepper, salt, and toss them nicely.

6. Roast them for about twenty to forty minutes (the roasting time depends on the size of the vegetables), accompanied by occasional tossing. Continue to roast until the carrots and parsnips become tender.

7. Finally, sprinkle some dill and serve.

Herbed Salmon

Total Prep & Cooking Time: 30 minutes

Yields: 4 servings

Nutrition Facts: Calories: 301 | Carbs: 1g | Protein: 29g | Fat: 19g | Fiber: 0g

Ingredients:

- Half a tsp. of dried thyme or two tsps. of freshly minced thyme
- Half a tsp. of pepper

- Three-fourth tsp. of salt
- One tbsp. of olive oil
- One tbsp. freshly minced rosemary or one tsp. of crushed dried rosemary.
- Four minced cloves of garlic
- Four (six ounces) fillets of salmon

Method:

1. At first, preheat your oven to 425 degrees.

2. Take a 15 by 10 by 1 inch baking pan and grease it.

3. Place the salmon on it while keeping the skin side down.

4. Combine the garlic cloves, rosemary, thyme, salt, and pepper. Spread it evenly over the salmon fillets.

5. Roast them for about fifteen to eighteen minutes until they reach your desired doneness.

Chipotle Cauliflower Tacos

Total Prep & Cooking Time: 30 minutes

Yields: 8 servings

Nutrition Facts: Calories: 440 | Carbs: 51.6g | Protein: 10.1g | Fat: 24g | Fiber: 9g

Ingredients:

For the tacos,

- Four tablespoons of avocado oil
- One head of cauliflower (large-sized, chopped into bite-sized florets)
- One cup of cilantro (freshly chopped)
- One tablespoon each of
  o Fresh lime juice
  o Maple syrup or honey
- Two tsps. of chipotle adobo sauce
- Cracked black pepper
- One teaspoon of salt
- 4-8 units of garlic cloves (freshly minced)

For the Chipotle Aioli,

- A quarter cup of chipotle adobo sauce
- Half a cup each of
  o Sour cream
  o Clean mayo
One teaspoon of sea salt

Two cloves of garlic (minced)

For serving,

- Almond flour tortillas
- Guacamole
- Almond ricotta cheese
- Sliced tomatoes, radish, and cabbage

Method:

1. Set the temperature of the oven to 425 degrees F. Now, use parchment paper to line a pan. Take the bite-sized florets of the cauliflower and spread them evenly on the pan. Use 2-4 tbsps. of avocado oil, pepper, salt, and minced garlic and drizzle it on the pan.

2. Roast the cauliflower for half an hour at 425 degrees F and halfway through the process, flip the florets.

3. When you are roasting the cauliflower, take the rest of the ingredients of the cauliflower and mix them in a bowl. Once everything has been properly incorporated, set the mixture aside.

4. Now, take another bowl and in it, add the ingredients of the chipotle aioli. Mix them and set the bowl aside.

5. If you have any other taco fixings, get them ready.

6. Once the cauliflower is ready, toss the florets in the chipotle sauce.

7. Serve the cauliflower in tortillas along with fixings of your choice and the chipotle aioli.

PART II

In this chapter, we are going to study the details of the reset diet and what recipes you can make.

Chapter 1: How to Reset Your Body?

Created by a celebrity trainer, Harley Pasternak, the body reset diet is a famous fifteen-day eating pattern that aims to jump-start weight loss. According to Pasternak, if you experience rapid loss in weight early in a diet, you will feel more motivated to stick to that diet plan. This theory is even supported by a few scientific studies (Alice A Gibson, 2017).

The body reset diet claims to help in weight loss with light exercise and low-calorie diet plans for fifteen days. The diet is divided into 3 phases of five days each. Each phase had a particular pattern of diet and exercise routine. You need to consume food five times every day, starting from the first phase, which mostly consists of smoothies and progressing to more solid foods in the second and third phases.

The three phases of the body reset diet are:

- **Phase One** – During this stage, you are required to consume only two snacks every day and drink smoothies for breakfast, lunch, and dinner. In the case of exercise, you have to walk at least ten thousand steps per day.

- **Phase Two** – During this phase, you can eat two snacks each day, consume solid food only once, and have to replace any two meals of the day with smoothies. In case of exercise, apart from walking ten thousand steps every day, on three of the days, you also have to finish five minutes of resistance training with the help of four separate exercises.

- **Phase Three** – You can consume two snacks every day, but you have to eat two low-calorie meals and replace one of your meals with a smoothie. For exercise, you are required to walk ten thousand steps. Apart from that, you also have to finish five minutes of resistance training with the help of four separate exercises each day.

After you have finished the standard fifteen-day diet requirements, you have to keep following the meal plan you followed in the third phase. However, during this time, you are allowed to have two "free meals" twice a week in which you can consume anything you want. These "free meals" are meant as a reward so that you can avoid feeling deprived. According to Pasternak, depriving yourself of a particular food continuously can result in binge eating (Nawal Alajmi, 2016).

There is no official endpoint of the diet after the first fifteen days for losing and maintaining weight. Pasternak suggests that the habits and routines formed over fifteen days should be maintained for a lifetime.

Chapter 2: Science Behind Metabolism Reset

Several people take on a "cleanse" or "detox" diet every year to lose the extra holiday weight or simply start following healthy habits. However, some fat diet plans are often a bit overwhelming. For example, it requires a tremendous amount of self-discipline to drink only juices. Moreover, even after finishing a grueling detox diet plan, you might just go back to eating foods that are bad for you because of those days of deprivation. New studies issued in the *Medicine & Science in Sports & Exercise* shows that low-calorie diets may result in binge eating, which is not the right method for lasting weight loss.

Another research conducted by the researchers at Loughborough University showed that healthy, college-aged women who followed a calorie-restricted diet consumed an extra three hundred calories at dinner as compared to the control group who consumed three standard meals. They revealed that it was because they had lower levels of peptide YY (represses appetite) and higher levels of ghrelin (makes you hungry). They are most likely to go hog wild when you are feeling ravenous, and it's finally time to eat (Nawal Alajmi K. D.-O., 2016).

Another research published in *Cognitive Neuroscience* studied the brains of chronic dieters. They revealed that there was a weaker connection between the two regions of the brain in people who had a higher percentage of body fat. They showed that they might have an increased risk of getting obese because it's harder for them to set their temptations aside (Pin-Hao Andy Chen, 2016).

A few other studies, however, also revealed that you could increase your self-control through practice. Self-control, similar to any other kind of strength, also requires time to develop. However, you can consider focusing on a diet plan that can help you "reset" instead of putting all your efforts into developing your self-control to get healthy.

A reset is considered as a new start – one that can get your metabolism and your liver in good shape. The liver is the biggest solid organ of your body, and it's mainly responsible for removing toxins that can harm your health and well-being by polluting your system. Toxins keep accumulating in your body all the time, and even though it's the liver's job to handle this, it can sometimes get behind schedule, which can result in inflammation. It causes a lot of strain on your metabolism and results in weight gain, particularly around the abdomen. The best method to alleviate this inflammation is to follow a metabolism rest diet and give your digestive system a vacation (Olivia M. Farr, 2015).

Chapter 3: Recipes for Smoothies and Salads

If you want to lose weight and you have a particular period within which you want to achieve it, then here are some recipes that are going to be helpful.

Green Smoothie

Total Prep & Cooking Time: 2 minutes

Yields: 1 serving

Nutrition Facts: Calories: 144 | Carbs: 28.2g | Protein: 3.4g | Fat: 2.9g | Fiber: 4.8g

Ingredients:

- One cup each of
  - Almond milk
  - Raw spinach
- One-third of a cup of strawberries
- One orange, peeled

Method:

1. Add the peeled orange, strawberries, almond milk, and raw spinach in a blender and blend everything until you get a smooth paste. You can add extra water if required to achieve the desired thickness.

2. Pour out the smoothie into a glass and serve.

Strawberry Banana Smoothie

Total Prep & Cooking Time: 5 minutes

Yields: 2 servings

Nutrition Facts: Calories: 198| Carbs: 30.8g | Protein: 5.9g | Fat: 7.1g | Fiber: 4.8g

Ingredients:

- Half a cup each of
  - Milk
  - Greek yogurt
- One banana, frozen and quartered
- Two cups of fresh strawberries, halved

Method:

1. Add the milk, Greek yogurt, banana, and strawberries into a high-powered blender and blend until you get a smooth mixture.

2. Pour the smoothie equally into two separate glasses and serve.

Notes:

- *Don't add ice to the smoothie as it can make it watery very quickly. Using frozen bananas will keep your smoothie cold.*

- *As you're using bananas and strawberries, there is no need to add any artificial sweetener.*

Salmon Citrus Salad

Total Prep & Cooking Time: 20 minutes

Yields: 6 servings

Nutrition Facts: Calories: 336 | Carbs: 20g | Protein: 17g | Fat: 21g | Fiber: 5g

Ingredients:

- One pound of Citrus Salmon (slow-roasted)
- Half of an English cucumber, sliced
- One tomato (large), sliced into a quarter of an inch thick pieces
- One grapefruit, peeled and cut into segments
- Two oranges, peeled and cut into segments
- Three beets, roasted and quartered
- One avocado
- Boston lettuce leaves
- Two tablespoons of red wine vinegar
- Half of a red onion
- Flakey salt
- Aleppo pepper flakes

For the Citrus Shallot Vinaigrette,

- Five tablespoons of olive oil (extra-virgin)
- One clove of garlic, smashed
- Salt and pepper
- One and a half tablespoons of rice wine vinegar
- Two tablespoons of orange juice or fresh lemon juice

- One tablespoon of shallot, minced

Method:

For preparing the Citrus Shallot Vinaigrette:

1. Add the ingredients for the vinaigrette in a bowl and whisk them together.

2. Keep the mixture aside.

For assembling the salad,

1. Add the onions and vinegar in a small bowl and pickle them by letting them sit for about fifteen minutes.

2. In the meantime, place the lettuce leaves on the serving plate.

3. Dice the avocado in half and eliminate the pit. Then scoop the flesh and add them onto the plate. Sprinkle a dash of flakey salt and Aleppo pepper on top to season it.

4. Add the quartered beets onto the serving plate along with the grapefruit and orange segments.

5. Salt the cucumber and tomato slices lightly and add them onto the plate.

6. Then, scatter the pickled onions on top and cut the salmon into bits and add it on the plate.

7. Lastly, drizzle the Citrus Shallot Vinaigrette on top of the salad and finish off with a dash of flakey salt.

Chapter 4: Quick and Easy Breakfast and Main Course Recipes

Quinoa Salad

Total Prep & Cooking Time: 40 minutes

Yields: Eight servings

Nutrition Facts: Calories: 205 | Carbs: 25.9g | Protein: 6.1g | Fat: 9.4g | Fiber: 4.6g

Ingredients:

- One tablespoon of red wine vinegar
- One-fourth of a cup each of
  - Lemon juice (about two to three lemons)
  - Olive oil
- One cup each of
  - Quinoa (uncooked), rinsed with the help of a fine-mesh colander
  - Flat-leaf parsley (from a single large bunch), finely chopped
- Three-fourth of a cup of red onion (one small red onion), chopped
- One red bell pepper (medium-sized), chopped
- One cucumber (medium-sized), seeded and chopped
- One and a half cups of chickpeas (cooked), or One can of chickpeas (about fifteen ounces), rinsed and drained
- Two cloves of garlic, minced or pressed
- Two cups of water
- Black pepper, freshly ground
- Half a teaspoon of fine sea salt

Method:

1. Place a medium-sized saucepan over medium-high heat and add the rinsed quinoa into it along with the water. Allow the mixture to boil and then reduce the heat and simmer it. Cook for about fifteen minutes so that the quinoa has absorbed all the water. As time goes on, decrease the heat and maintain a gentle simmer. Take the saucepan away from the heat and cover it with a lid. Allow the cooked quinoa to rest for about five minutes to give it some time to increase in size.

2. Add the onions, bell pepper, cucumber, chickpeas, and parsley in a large serving bowl and mix them together. Keep the mixture aside.

3. Add the garlic, vinegar, lemon juice, olive oil, and salt in another small bowl and whisk the ingredients so that they are appropriately combined. Keep this mixture aside.

4. When the cooked quinoa has almost cooled down, transfer it to the serving bowl. Add the dressing on top and toss to combine everything together.

5. Add an extra pinch of sea salt and the black pepper to season according to your preference. Allow the salad to rest for five to ten minutes before serving it for the best results.

6. You can keep the salad in the refrigerator for up to four days. Make sure to cover it properly.

7. You can serve it at room temperature or chilled.

Notes: Instead of cooking additional quinoa, you can use about three cups of leftover quinoa for making this salad. Moreover, you can also serve this salad with fresh greens and an additional drizzle of lemon juice and olive oil. You can also add a dollop of cashew sour cream or crumbled feta cheese as a topping.

Herb and Goat Cheese Omelet

Total Prep & Cooking Time: 20 minutes

Yields: Two servings

Nutrition Facts: Calories: 233 | Carbs: 3.6g | Protein: 16g | Fat: 17.6g | Fiber: 1g

Ingredients:

- Half a cup each of
  - Red bell peppers (3 x quarter-inch), julienne-cut
  - Zucchini, thinly sliced
- Four large eggs
- Two teaspoons of olive oil, divided
- One-fourth of a cup of goat cheese (one ounce), crumbled
- Half a teaspoon of fresh tarragon, chopped
- One teaspoon each of
  - Fresh parsley, chopped
  - Fresh chives, chopped
- One-eighth of a teaspoon of salt
- One-fourth of a teaspoon of black pepper, freshly ground (divided)
- One tablespoon of water

Method:

1. Break the eggs into a bowl and add one tablespoon of water into it. Whisk them together and add in one-eighth of a teaspoon each of salt and ground black pepper.

2. In another small bowl, mix the goat cheese, tarragon, and parsley and keep it aside.

3. Place a nonstick skillet over medium heat and heat one teaspoon of olive oil in it. Add in the sliced zucchini, bell pepper, and the remaining one-eighth of a teaspoon of black pepper along with a dash of salt. Cook for about four minutes so that the bell pepper and zucchini get soft. Transfer the zucchini-bell pepper mixture onto a plate and cover it with a lid to keep it warm.

4. Add about half a teaspoon of oil into a skillet and add in half of the whisked egg into it. Do not stir the eggs and let the egg set slightly. Loosen the set edges of the omelet carefully with the help of a spatula. Tilt the skillet to move the uncooked part of the egg to the side. Keep following this method for about five seconds so that there is no more runny egg in the skillet. Add half of the crumbled goat cheese mixture evenly over the omelet and let it cook for another minute so that it sets.

5. Transfer the omelet onto a plate and fold it into thirds.

6. Repeat the process with the rest of the egg mixture, half a teaspoon of olive oil, and the goat cheese mixture.

7. Add the chopped chives on top of the omelets and serve with the bell pepper and zucchini mixture.

Mediterranean Cod

Total Prep & Cooking Time: 15 minutes

Yields: 4 servings

Nutrition Facts: Calories: 320 | Carbs: 31g | Protein: 35g | Fat: 8g | Fiber: 8g

Ingredients:

- One pound of spinach
- Four fillets of cod (almost one and a half pounds)
- Two zucchinis (medium-sized), chopped
- One cup of marinara sauce
- One-fourth of a teaspoon of red pepper, crushed
- Two cloves of garlic, chopped
- One tablespoon of olive oil
- Salt and pepper, according to taste
- Whole wheat roll, for serving

Method:

1. Place a ten-inch skillet on medium heat and add the marinara sauce and zucchini into it. Combine them together and let it simmer on medium heat.

2. Add the fillets of cod into the simmering sauce. Add one-fourth of a teaspoon each of salt and pepper too. Cover the skillet with a lid and let it cook for about seven minutes so that the cod gets just opaque throughout.

3. In the meantime, place a five-quart saucepot on medium heat and heat the olive oil in it. Add in the crushed red pepper and minced garlic. Stir and cook for about a minute.

4. Then, add in the spinach along with one-eighth of a teaspoon of salt. Cover the saucepot with a lid and let it cook for about five minutes, occasionally stirring so that the spinach gets wilted.

5. Add the spinach on the plates and top with the sauce and cod mixture and serve with the whole wheat roll.

Grilled Chicken and Veggies

Total Prep & Cooking Time: 35 minutes

Yields: 4 servings

Nutrition Facts: Calories: 305 | Carbs: 11g | Protein: 26g | Fat: 17g | Fiber: 3g

Ingredients:

For the marinade,

- Four cloves of garlic, crushed

- One-fourth of a cup each of
  - o Fresh lemon juice
  - o Olive oil
- One teaspoon each of
  - o Salt
  - o Smoked paprika
  - o Dried oregano
- Black pepper, according to taste
- Half a teaspoon of red chili flakes

For the grilling,

- Two to three zucchinis or courgette (large), cut into thin slices
- Twelve to sixteen spears of asparagus, woody sides trimmed
- Broccoli
- Two bell peppers, seeds eliminated and cut into thin slices
- Four pieces of chicken breasts (large), skinless and de-boned

Method:

1. Preheat your griddle or grill pan.

2. Sprinkle some salt on top of the chicken breasts to season them. Keep them aside to rest while you prepare the marinade.

3. For the marinade, mix all the ingredients properly.

4. Add about half of the marinade over the vegetables and the other half over the seasoned chicken breasts. Allow the marinade to rest for a couple of minutes.

5. Place the chicken pieces on the preheated grill. Grill for about five to seven minutes on each side until they are cooked according to your preference. The time on the grill depends on the thickness of the chicken breasts.

6. Remove them from the grill and cover them using a foil. Set it aside to rest and prepare to grill the vegetables in the meantime.

7. Grill the vegetables for a few minutes until they begin to char and are crispy yet tender.

8. Remove them from the grill and transfer them onto a serving plate. Serve the veggies along with the grilled chicken and add the lemon wedges on the side for squeezing.

Notes: *You can add as much or as little vegetables as you like. The vegetable amounts are given only as a guide. Moreover, feel free to replace some of them with the vegetables you like to eat.*

Stuffed Peppers

Total Prep & Cooking Time: 50 minutes

Yields: 4 servings

Nutrition Facts: Calories: 438 | Carbs: 32g | Protein: 32g | Fat: 20g | Fiber: 5g

Ingredients:

For the stuffed peppers,

- One pound of ground chicken or turkey
- Four bell peppers (large) of any color
- One and a quarter of a cups of cheese, shredded
- One and a half cups of brown rice, cooked (you can use cauliflower rice or quinoa)
- One can (about fourteen ounces) of fire-roasted diced tomatoes along with its juices
- Two teaspoons of olive oil (extra-virgin)
- One teaspoon each of
  o Garlic powder
  o Ground cumin
- One tablespoon of ground chili powder
- One-fourth of a teaspoon of black pepper
- Half a teaspoon of kosher salt

For serving,

- Sour cream or Greek yogurt

- Salsa

- Freshly chopped cilantro

- Avocado, sliced

- Freshly squeezed lemon juice

Method:

1. Preheat your oven to 375 degrees Fahrenheit.

2. Take a nine by thirteen-inch baking dish and coat it lightly with a nonstick cooking spray.

3. Take the bell peppers and slice them from top to bottom into halves. Remove the membranes and the seeds. Keep the bell peppers in the baking dish with the cut-side facing upwards.

4. Place a large, nonstick skillet on medium-high heat and heat the olive oil in it. Add in the chicken, pepper, salt, garlic powder, ground cumin, and chili powder and cook for about four minutes so that the chicken is cooked through and gets brown. Break apart the chicken while it's cooking. Drain off any excess liquid and then add in the can of diced tomatoes along with the juices. Allow it to simmer for a minute.

5. Take the pan away from the heat. Add in the cooked rice along with three-fourth of a cup of the shredded cheese and stir everything together.

6. Add this filling inside the peppers and add the remaining shredded cheese as a topping.

7. Add a little amount of water into the pan containing the peppers so that it barely covers the bottom of the pan.

8. Keep it uncovered and bake it in the oven for twenty-five to thirty-five minutes so that the cheese gets melted and the peppers get soft.

9. Add any of your favorite fixings as a topping and serve hot.

Notes:

- *For preparing the stuffed peppers ahead of time, make sure to allow the rice and chicken mixture to cool down completely before filling the peppers. You can prepare the stuffed peppers before time, and then you have to cover it with a lid and keep it in the refrigerator for a maximum of twenty-four hours before baking the peppers.*

- *If you're planning to reheat the stuffed peppers, gently reheat them in your oven or microwave. If you're using a microwave for this purpose, make sure to cut the peppers into pieces to warm them evenly.*

- *You can store any leftovers in the freezer for up to three months. Alternatively, you can keep them in the refrigerator for up to four days. Allow it to thaw in the fridge overnight.*

Brussels Sprouts With Honey Mustard Chicken

Total Prep & Cooking Time: Fifty minutes

Yields: Four servings

Nutrition Facts: Calories: 360 | Carbs: 14.5g | Protein: 30.8g | Fat: 20g | Fiber: 3.7g

Ingredients:

- One and a half pounds of Brussels sprouts, divided into two halves
- Two pounds of chicken thighs, skin-on and bone-in (about four medium-sized thighs)
- Three cloves of garlic, minced
- One-fourth of a large onion, cut into slices
- One tablespoon each of
  - Honey
  - Whole-grain mustard
  - Dijon mustard
- Two tablespoons of freshly squeezed lemon juice (one lemon)
- One-fourth of a cup plus two tablespoons of olive oil (extra-virgin)
- Freshly ground black pepper
- Kosher salt
- Non-stick cooking spray

Method:

1. Preheat your oven to 425 degrees Fahrenheit.

2. Take a large baking sheet and grease it with nonstick cooking spray. Keep it aside.

3. Add the minced garlic, honey, whole-grain mustard, Dijon mustard, one tablespoon of the lemon juice, one-fourth cup of the olive oil in a medium-sized bowl and mix them together. Add the Kosher salt and black pepper to season according to your preference.

4. Dip the chicken thighs into the sauce with the help of tongs and coat both sides. Transfer the things on the baking sheet. You can get rid of any extra sauce.

5. Mix the red onion and Brussels sprouts in a medium-sized bowl and drizzle one tablespoon of lemon juice along with the remaining two tablespoons of olive oil onto it. Toss everything together until the vegetables are adequately coated.

6. Place the red onion-Brussels sprouts mixture on the baking sheet around the chicken pieces. Ensure that the chicken and vegetables are not overlapping.

7. Sprinkle a little amount of salt and pepper on the top and keep it in the oven to roast for about thirty to thirty-five minutes so that the Brussels sprouts get crispy and the chicken has an internal temperature of 165 degrees Fahrenheit and has turned golden brown.

8. Serve hot.

Quinoa Stuffed Chicken

Total Prep & Cooking Time: 50 minutes

Yields: Four servings

Nutrition Facts: Calories: 355 | Carbs: 28g | Protein: 30g | Fat: 13g | Fiber: 4g

Ingredients:

- One and a half cups of chicken broth
- Three-fourths of a cup of quinoa (any color of your choice)
- Four chicken breasts (boneless and skinless)
- One lime, zested and one tablespoon of lime juice
- One-fourth of a cup of cilantro, chipped
- One-third of a cup of unsweetened coconut, shaved or coconut chips
- One Serrano pepper, seeded and diced
- Two cloves of garlic, minced
- Half a cup of red onion, diced
- Three-fourth of a cup of bell pepper, diced
- One tablespoon of coconut oil
- One teaspoon each of
  - Salt
  - Chili powder
  - Ground cumin

Method:

1. Preheat your oven to 375 degrees Fahrenheit.

2. Take a rimmed baking sheet and line it with parchment paper.

3. Place a medium-sized saucepan over medium-high heat and add the coconut oil in it. After it has melted, add in the Serrano peppers, garlic, red onion, and bell pepper and sauté for about one to two minutes so that they soften just a bit. Make sure that the vegetables are still bright in color. Then transfer the cooked vegetables into a bowl.

4. Add the quinoa in the empty sauce pot and increase the heat to high. Pour the chicken broth in it along with half a teaspoon of salt. Close the lid of the pot and bring it to a boil, allowing the quinoa to cook for about fifteen minutes so that the surface of the quinoa develops vent holes, and the broth has absorbed completely. Take the pot away from the heat and allow it to steam for an additional five minutes.

5. In the meantime, cut a slit along the long side in each chicken breast. It will be easier with the help of a boning knife. You are making a deep pocket in each breast, having a half-inch border around the remaining three attached sides. Keep the knife parallel to the cutting board and cut through the middle of the breast and leaving the opposite side attached. Try to cut it evenly as it's challenging to cook thick uncut portions properly in the oven. After that, add salt, cumin, and chili powder on all sides of the chicken.

6. When the quinoa has turned fluffy, add in the lime juice, lime zest, shaved coconut, and sautéed vegetables and stir them in. Taste the mixture and adjust the salt as per your preference.

7. Add the confetti quinoa mixture inside the cavity of the chicken breast. Place the stuffed breasts on the baking sheet with the quinoa facing upwards. They'll look like open envelopes.

8. Bake them in the oven for about twenty minutes.

9. Serve warm.

Kale and Sweet Potato Frittata

Total Prep & Cooking Time: 30 minutes

Yields: 4 servings

Nutrition Facts: Calories: 144 | Carbs: 10g | Protein: 7g | Fat: 9g | Fiber: 2g

Ingredients:

- Three ounces of goat cheese
- Two cloves of garlic
- Half of a red onion (small)
- Two cups each of
  - Sweet potatoes
  - Firmly packed kale, chopped
- Two tablespoons of olive oil
- One cup of half-and-half
- Six large eggs
- Half a teaspoon of pepper, freshly ground
- One teaspoon of Kosher salt

Method:

1. Preheat your oven to 350 degrees Fahrenheit.

2. Add the eggs, half-and-half, salt, and black pepper in a bowl and whisk everything together.

3. Place a ten-inch ovenproof nonstick skillet over medium heat and add one tablespoon of oil in it. Sauté the sweet potatoes in the skillet for about eight to ten minutes so that they turn soft and golden brown. Transfer them onto a plate and keep warm.

4. Next, add in the remaining one tablespoon of oil and sauté the kale along with the red onions and garlic in it for about three to four minutes so that the kale gets soft and wilted. Then, add in the whisked egg mixture evenly over the vegetables and cook for an additional three minutes.

5. Add some goat cheese on the top and bake it in the oven for ten to fourteen minutes so that it sets.

Walnut, Ginger, and Pineapple Oatmeal

Total Prep & Cooking Time: 30 minutes

Yields: 4 servings

Nutrition Facts: Calories: 323 | Carbs: 61g | Protein: 6g | Fat: 8g | Fiber: 5g

Ingredients:

- Two large eggs
- Two cups each of
  o Fresh pineapple, coarsely chopped
  o Old-fashioned rolled oats
  o Whole milk
- One cup of walnuts, chopped

75

- Half a cup of maple syrup
- One piece of ginger
- Two teaspoons of vanilla extract
- Half a teaspoon of salt

Method:

1. Preheat your oven to 400 degrees Fahrenheit.

2. Add the ginger, walnuts, pineapple, oats, and salt in a large bowl and mix them together. Add the mixture evenly among four ten-ounce ramekins and keep them aside.

3. Whisk the eggs along with the milk, maple syrup, and vanilla extract in a medium-sized bowl. Pour one-quarter of this mixture into each ramekin containing the oat-pineapple mixture.

4. Keep the ramekins on the baking sheet and bake them in the oven for about twenty-five minutes until the oats turn light golden brown on the top and have set properly.

5. Serve with some additional maple syrup on the side.

Caprese Salad

Total Prep & Cooking Time: 15 minutes

Yields: 4 servings

Nutrition Facts: Calories: 216 | Carbs: 4g | Protein: 13g | Fat: 16g | Fiber: 1g

Ingredients:

For the salad,

- Nine basil leaves (medium-sized)
- Eight ounces of fresh whole-milk mozzarella cheese
- Two tomatoes (medium-sized)
- One-fourth of a teaspoon of black pepper, freshly ground
- Half a teaspoon of Kosher salt, or one-fourth of a teaspoon of sea salt

For the dressing,

- One teaspoon of Dijon mustard
- One tablespoon each of
  o Balsamic vinegar
  o Olive oil

Method:

1. Add the olive oil, balsamic vinegar, and Dijon mustard into a small bowl and whisk them together with the help of a small hand whisk so that you get a smooth salad dressing. Keep it aside.

2. Cut the tomatoes into thin slices and try to get ten slices in total.

3. Cut the mozzarella into nine thin slices with the help of a sharp knife.

4. Place the slices of tomatoes and mozzarella on a serving plate, alternating and overlapping one another. Then, add the basil leaves on the top.

5. Season the salad with black pepper and salt and drizzle the prepared dressing on top.

6. Serve immediately.

One-Pot Chicken Soup

Total Prep & Cooking Time: 30 minutes

Yields: 6 servings

Nutrition Facts: Calories: 201 | Carbs: 20g | Protein: 16g | Fat: 7g | Fiber: 16g

Ingredients:

- Three cups of loosely packed chopped kale (or other greens of your choice)
- Two cups of chicken, shredded

- One can of white beans (about fifteen ounces), slightly drained

- Eight cups of broth (vegetable broth or chicken broth)

- Four cloves of garlic, minced

- One cup of yellow or white onion, diced

- One tablespoon of avocado oil (skip if you are using bacon)

- One strip of uncured bacon, chopped (optional)

- Black pepper + sea salt, according to taste

Method:

1. Place a Dutch oven or a large pot over medium heat. When it gets hot, add in the oil or bacon (optional), stirring occasionally, and allow it to get hot for about a minute.

2. Then, add in the diced onion and sauté for four to five minutes, occasionally stirring so that the onions get fragrant and translucent. Add in the minced garlic next and sauté for another two to three minutes. Be careful so as not to burn the ingredients.

3. Then, add the chicken, slightly drained white beans, and broth and bring the mixture to a simmer. Cook for about ten minutes to bring out all the flavors. Taste the mixture and add salt and pepper to season according to your preference. Add in the chopped kale in the last few minutes of cooking. Cover the pot and let it cook until the kale has wilted.

4. Serve hot.

Notes: You can store any leftovers in the freezer for up to a month. Or, you can store them in the refrigerator for a maximum of three to four days. Simply reheat on the stovetop or in the microwave and eat it later.

Chocolate Pomegranate Truffles

Total Prep & Cooking Time: 10 minutes

Yields: Twelve to Fourteen truffles

Nutrition Facts: Calories: 95 | Carbs: 26g | Protein: 1g | Fat: 2g | Fiber: 3g

Ingredients:

- One-third of a cup of pomegranate arils
- Half a teaspoon each of
  - Vanilla extract
  - Ground cinnamon
- Half a cup of ground flax seed
- Two tablespoons of cocoa powder (unsweetened)
- About one tablespoon of water
- One and a half cups of pitted Medjool dates
- One-eighth of a teaspoon of salt

Method:

1. Add the pitted dates in a food processor and blend until it begins to form a ball. Add some water and pulse again. Add in the vanilla, cinnamon, flax seeds, cocoa powder, and salt and blend until everything is combined properly.

2. Turn off the food processor and unplug it. Add in the pomegranate arils and fold them in the mixture so that they are distributed evenly.

3. Make twelve to fourteen balls using the mixture. You can create an outer coating or topping if you want by rolling the balls in finely shredded coconut or cocoa powder.

Notes: *You can store the chocolate pomegranate truffles in the fridge in an air-tight container for a maximum of three days.*

PART III

Pumpkin Pancakes

Total Prep & Cooking Time: 40 minutes

Yields: 2 servings

Nutrition Facts: Calories: 183 | Carbs: 39g | Protein: 5.4g | Fat: 1.2g | Sodium: 130mg

Ingredients:

- Two egg whites
- Two tsps. of pumpkin pie spice
- One tsp. of baking powder
- One tbsp. of brown sugar
- Three packets of Stevia
- 1.25 cups of all-purpose flour
- Two cups each of
  - Rice milk
  - Salt-free pumpkin puree

Method:

1. Start by mixing all the dry ingredients together in a bowl – baking powder, Stevia, sugar, flour, and pumpkin pie spice.

2. Now, take another bowl and, in it, mix the rice milk and pumpkin puree thoroughly.

3. In another bowl, form stiff peaks by whipping egg whites.

4. Take the mixture of dry ingredients and add them to the wet ingredients. Blend them in. Once you get a smooth mixture, add the egg whites, and whip them.

5. Grill the mixture on an oiled griddle on medium flame.

6. When you notice bubbles forming on the pancakes, you have to flip them.

7. Cook both sides of the pancakes evenly so that they turn golden brown.

Pasta Salad

Total Prep & Cooking Time: 50 minutes

Yields: 4 servings (half a cup each serving)

Nutrition Facts: Calories: 69 | Carbs: 12.5g | Protein: 2.5g | Fat: 1.3g | Sodium: 72mg

Ingredients:

- A quarter cup of olives (sliced after being pitted)
- One cup of chopped cauliflower
- Two cups of fusilli pasta (cooked)
- Half a unit each of
  - Green bell pepper (sliced)
  - Red onion (chopped)
  - Tomato (small-sized, diced)

Method:

1. Start by cooking the pasta, and for that, you have to follow the directions as mentioned on the package.

2. Now, drain the pasta. Add all the vegetables.

3. Choose any dressing of your choice, but it has to be low-fat. Toss the pasta and the veggies in the dressing.

4. Serve and enjoy!

Broccoli and Apple Salad

Total Prep & Cooking Time: 15 minutes

Yields: 8 servings (3/4 cup each serving)

Nutrition Facts: Calories: 160 | Carbs: 18g | Protein: 4g | Fat: 8g | Sodium: 63mg

Ingredients:

- Four cups of fresh florets of broccoli
- One medium-sized apple
- Half a cup each of
  - Sweetened cranberries (dried)
  - Red onion
- A quarter cup each of
  - Walnuts
  - Fresh parsley
  - Mayonnaise
- Two tbsps. each of
  - Apple cider vinegar
  - Honey
- A three-fourth cup of plain Greek yogurt (low-fat)

Method:

1. Prepare the broccoli florets by cutting into bite-sized chunks. Trim them properly. Take the apple and cut into small pieces as well but in the unpeeled state. Prepare the parsley by chopping them coarsely.

2. Now, take a large-sized bowl and add the mayonnaise, yogurt, vinegar, honey, and parsley. Whisk them together.

3. Take the remaining ingredients and add them too. Make sure they are evenly coated with the yogurt mixture. Once prepared, keep the salad in the refrigerator because it is best served when chilled. It allows the flavors to combine properly. Before serving, stir the salad.

Notes:

- *You can use your favorite type of apple.*

- *If you want, you can sprinkle some more parsley on top just before serving.*

Pineapple Frangelico Sorbet

Total Prep & Cooking Time: 2 hours 10 minutes

Yields: 4 servings

Nutrition Facts: Calories: 119 | Carbs: 28g | Protein: 1g | Fat: 0.2g | Sodium: 2.4mg

Ingredients:

- Two tsps. of Stevia
- One tbsp. of Frangelico (keep two tsps. extra)
- Half a cup of unsweetened pineapple juice
- Two cups of pineapple (fresh)

Method:

1. Take all the ingredients in the container of the blender and process them until you get a smooth mixture.

2. Then, take this mixture and divide it into ice cubes. Keep it in the refrigerator and allow it to freeze.

3. When you find that the mixture has frozen, take them out and blend them in the food processor again. This process will give you a fluffy texture.

4. Before you serve, refreeze the sorbet.

Egg Muffins

Total Prep & Cooking Time: 45 minutes

Yields: 8 servings

Nutrition Facts: Calories: 154 | Carbs: 3g | Protein: 12g | Fat: 10g | Sodium: 155mg

Ingredients:

- Half an lb. of ground pork
- Half a tsp. of herb seasoning blend of your choice
- A quarter tsp. of salt
- Eight eggs (large-sized)
- A quarter tsp. each of
  o Onion powder
  o Garlic powder
  o Poultry seasoning
- One cup each of
  o Onion
  o Bell peppers (A mixture of orange, yellow, and red)

Method:

1. Set the oven temperature to 350 degrees F and use cooking spray to coat a muffin tin of regular size.

2. Prepare the onions and bell peppers by dicing them finely.

3. Take a bowl and in it, combine the following ingredients – garlic powder, poultry seasoning, pork, onion powder, and herb seasoning blend. Form the sausage by combining all of this properly.

4. Now cook the sausage in a non-stick skillet. Once it has been appropriately cooked, drain the sausage.

5. Use salt and milk substitute/milk to beat the eggs in a bowl. In it, add the veggies and the sausage mix.

6. Take the prepared muffin tin and pour the egg mixture into it. You have to leave enough space for the muffins so that they can rise. Bake them for about 20-22 minutes.

Notes: *If there are extra muffins, then you can have them as a quick breakfast the next day, and you simply have to reheat them for about 40 seconds.*

Linguine With Broccoli, Chickpeas, and Ricotta

Total Prep & Cooking Time: 1 hour 5 minutes

Yields: 4 servings

Nutrition Facts: Calories: 404 | Carbs: 49.8g | Protein: 13.2g | Fat: 17.5g | Sodium: 180.4mg

Ingredients:

- Eight ounces of ricotta cheese that have been kept at room temperature
- A bunch of Tuscan kale (chopped into bite-sized chunks and stemmed)
- One-third cup of extra-virgin olive oil
- A pinch of black pepper
- Two cloves of garlic (sliced thinly)
- Fourteen ounces of chickpeas (rinsed after draining)
- Twelve ounces of spaghetti or linguine pasta
- A pinch of kosher salt
- One lemon
- Half a teaspoon of red pepper flakes
- Two tablespoons of unsalted butter
- To taste – Flaky sea salt

Method:

1. Take a large pot and add water to it. Add salt and bring the water to a boil. Cook the pasta by following the directions mentioned on the package. They must be perfectly al dente. Once the pasta is done, you have to drain it but, at the same time, reserve half a cup of the cooking water.

2. Heat the broiler and adjust the rack. Toss the following ingredients together in a bowl – garlic, chickpeas, broccoli, one-third cup of oil, and red pepper flakes. Everything should become evenly coated. Use pepper and salt to season the mixture.

3.   Take a sheet pan and spread the mixture out on it evenly.

4.   Take the kale and add it to the previous bowl you used. Toss it again along with the remaining oil, if any. If you need it, then you can drizzle some more oil on top. Spread the kale in a second sheet pan in an even layer.

5.   You have to take one sheet at a time while working. Broil the chickpeas and broccoli and halfway through the process, toss them. The broccoli should become charred and tender, and the chickpeas should be toasty. It will take about seven minutes. Then, broil the kale too for about five minutes, and they should become crispy.

6.   Take the lemon, zest it, and then cut it into two halves. Take one half and form four wedges out of it. The juice of the lemon will have to be squeezed out on the roasted veggies and then use pepper and salt to season.

7.   Place the pasta back in the pot. Take the pasta water you had earlier reserved and add it to the pasta and the lemon zest, butter, and ricotta. Keep tossing so that everything is well incorporated. Now, add the roasted veggies too. If you need, add some more pasta water while tossing.

8.   Now, your linguine is done, and you have to divide it among four bowls—season with pepper and flaky sea salt. Squeeze a few drops of lemon on top and serve. If you want, drizzle some more oil before serving.

Ground Beef Soup
Total Prep & Cooking Time: 35 minutes

Yields: 6 servings

Nutrition Facts: Calories: 222 | Carbs: 19g | Protein: 20g | Fat: 8g | Sodium: 170mg

Ingredients:

- Half a cup of onion
- One tbsp. of sour cream
- Three cups of mixed vegetables (frozen, peas, green beans, corn, and carrots)
- One-third cup of uncooked white rice
- Two cups of water
- One cup of beef broth (reduced-sodium variety)
- One tsp. of browning sauce and seasoning of your choice
- Two tsps. of lemon pepper seasoning of your choice
- One lb. of ground beef (lean)

Method:

1. Prepare the onion by chopping them thoroughly. Then, take a large-sized saucepan and, in it, brown the onion and ground beef together. Drain the juices and excess fat.

2. Add the browning sauce and seasonings. Then, add the mixed veggies, rice, water, and beef broth and mix everything together.

3. Bring the mixture to a boil after placing it on high flame. Once the mixture starts boiling, reduce the flame to medium-low and cover the saucepan. Allow it to simmer and cook it for half an hour.

4. Once done, remove the pan from the flame and add the sour cream. Stir it in and serve.

Apple Oatmeal Crisp

Total Prep & Cooking Time: 40 minutes

Yields: 8 servings

Nutrition Facts: Calories: 297 | Carbs: 42g | Protein: 3g | Fat: 13g | Sodium: 95mg

Ingredients:

- A three-quarter cup of brown sugar
- Half a cup of butter
- One tsp. of cinnamon
- Half a cup of all-purpose flour
- Five apples (if possible, then Granny Smith ones)
- One cup of whole oatmeal

Method:

1. Set the temperature of the oven to 350 degrees F and preheat. Peel the apples, core them, and then cut them into slices.

2. Take a bowl and then mix the following ingredients in it together – brown sugar, oatmeal, cinnamon, and flour.

3. Use a pastry cutter to cut the butter into the oatmeal and make sure they are well blended.

4. Take a baking pan of 9 by 9 inches in size and place the sliced apples in it.

5. Take the oatmeal mixture and sprinkle it on top of the apples.

6. Bake the mixture for about thirty to thirty-five minutes.

Chapter 2: Weekend Recipes for Renal Diet

Hawaiian Chicken Salad Sandwich
Total Prep & Cooking Time: 10 minutes + chilling

Yields: 4 servings

Nutrition Facts: Calories: 349 | Carbs: 24g | Protein: 22g | Fat: 17g | Sodium: 398mg

Ingredients:

- One cup of pineapple tidbits
- Two cups of cooked chicken
- One-third cup of carrots
- Half a cup each of
    o   Green bell pepper
    o   Mayonnaise (low-fat)
- Four units of flatbread
- Half a tsp. of black pepper

Method:

1. Take the cooked chicken and chop it into bite-sized pieces.

2. Prepare the pineapple by draining it and then shred the carrots and chop the bell pepper.

3. Take all the ingredients in a medium-sized bowl and mix them well.

4. Refrigerate the mixture until it is thoroughly chilled.

5. Before serving, spread the chicken on the flatbread's open surface, or if you prefer it wrapped, you can use a tortilla too.

Apple Puffs

Total Prep & Cooking Time: 1 hour 20 minutes

Yields: 12 servings

Nutrition Facts: Calories: 156 | Carbs: 22g | Protein: 1.5g | Fat: 7.3g | Sodium: 176mg

Ingredients:

- Eight ounces of puff dough sheets
- One can (21 oz.) of apple pie filling
- Half a tsp. of rum extract
- One tsp. each of
  - Powdered sugar
  - Baking soda
  - Ground cinnamon

Method:

1. First, you have to thaw the puff dough sheets at room temperature, and it will take you approximately 1 hour.

2. Set the temperature of the oven to 400 degrees F and preheat.

3. Take a bowl, and in it, add the apple pie filling. If you have already sliced the apples, then you can form thirds from them now. Mix the rum extract and cinnamon with the apples.

4. Once the dough has been completely thawed, take one of the sheets and cut nine equal squares from it. Take the other sheet, and you will need only one-third of it to cut another three such squares.

5. Now, take the muffin tin and place the squares in each of the tins. In each of these squares, spoon some of the apple mixture.

6. Bake the preparation in the preheated oven for fifteen minutes, and they should become golden brown in color.

7. Once done, remove the puffs from the muffin tins and before serving, sprinkle some powdered sugar on top of each apple puff. Serve them warm.

Creamy Orzo and Vegetables

Total Prep & Cooking Time: 30 minutes

Yields: 6 servings

Nutrition Facts: Calories: 176 | Carbs: 25g | Protein: 10g | Fat: 4g | Sodium: 193mg

Ingredients:

- Half a cup of frozen green peas
- One tsp. of curry powder
- One carrot (medium-sized)
- One zucchini (small-sized)
- One onion (small-sized)
- One clove of garlic
- Three cups of chicken broth (low-sodium variety)
- Two tbsps. each of
    - Olive oil
    - Fresh parsley
- A quarter tsp. of black pepper
- A quarter cup of Parmesan cheese (freshly grated)
- One cup of cooked orzo pasta
- A quarter tsp. of salt

Method:

1. Start by preparing the veggies. Chop the zucchini and onion. Chop the garlic finely. Then, take the carrots and shred them.

2. Place a large-sized skillet on the oven over medium flame. Heat olive oil in the skillet. Sauté the following ingredients in it for about five minutes – carrots, zucchini, onion, and garlic.

3. After that, add the curry powder to the mixture. Season with salt and then add the chicken broth. Bring the mixture to a boil.

4. Now, add the cooked orzo pasta and keep stirring until the mixture starts boiling. Cover the skillet and allow the mixture to simmer. Keep stirring from time to time and cook the pasta for another 10 minutes. By this time, the pasta will become al dente, and the liquid will be absorbed.

5. Add the chopped parsley, cheese, and the frozen peas into the pasta. Keep heating until the vegetables are sufficiently hot, and if you want to enhance the creaminess, then you can add some more broth—season with pepper.

Minestrone Soup

Total Prep & Cooking Time: 45 minutes

Yields: 4 servings

Nutrition Facts: Calories: 144 | Carbs: 21.9g | Protein: 5.9g | Fat: 4.3g | Sodium: 55.1mg

Ingredients:

- Four cups of low-sodium chicken broth (low-fat)
- One carrot (large-sized)
- One and a half cups of dry macaroni (elbow-shaped)
- 14 oz. of tomatoes (diced, without any salt content)
- Two stalks of celery
- Two garlic cloves
- Half a cup of zucchini (freshly chopped)
- One teaspoon each of
  - Dried basil
  - Dried oregano
  - Freshly ground black pepper
- Half an onion (large-sized)
- One can of green snap beans (without any salt content)
- Two tbsps. of olive oil

Method:

1. Prepare the veggies by dicing zucchini, garlic, and onion. Then, take the carrots and shred them. Either use fresh green beans or canned ones, but you have to cut them into pieces of half an inch size.

2. Take a Dutch oven or a large pot and place it on medium flame—heat olive oil in the pot. Add the diced onions in the pot as well and then cook them for a couple of minutes until they become translucent.

3. Add zucchini, carrot, celery, and garlic, and if you are using fresh green beans, then add them too. Cook the vegetables for about five minutes and they will become tender.

4. Add black pepper, oregano, basil, and if you are using canned beans, then add them now.

5. Add the chicken broth and the diced tomatoes and keep stirring.

6. Bring the mixture to a boil and once it starts boiling, allow the mixture to simmer for about ten minutes.

7. Add the pasta and cook them for an additional ten minutes by following the directions mentioned on the package.

8. Before serving, garnish the pasta with fresh basil on top. Serve into bowls and enjoy!

Frosted Grapes

Total Prep & Cooking Time: 1 hour 5 minutes

Yields: 10 servings (serving size – half a cup)

Nutrition Facts: Calories: 88 | Carbs: 21g | Protein: 1g | Fat: 0g | Sodium: 41mg

Ingredients:

- Three oz. of flavored gelatin
- Five cups of seedless grapes

Method:

1. De-steam the seedless grapes after you have washed them. After that, let them be but make sure they are slightly damp.

2. In a large-sized bowl, add the dry gelatin mix. Remember that you shouldn't be pouring in water.

3. Add these damp grapes into the bowl, and in order to coat them uniformly, toss them well.

4. Now, take a baking sheet, and place these grapes on the sheet in an even layer.

5. Freeze them for 1 hour and then serve chilled.

Notes: *The flavor of the gelatin you use can be adjusted as per your choice. If you want to decrease the carbs, then use gelatin that is sugar-free.*

Yogurt and Fruit Salad

Total Prep & Cooking Time: 2 hours 20 minutes

Yields: 4 servings

Nutrition Facts: Calories: 99 | Carbs: 22g | Protein: 2.6g | Fat: 0.7g | Sodium: 12mg

Ingredients:

- One-third cup of dried cranberries
- Half a cup of pineapple chunks (fresh)
- Six strawberries (large-sized)
- Six ounces of Greek yogurt (strawberry flavored)
- Four ounces of mandarin oranges (drained, light syrup)
- Ten green grapes
- One apple (with skin, medium-sized)

Method:

1. Wash the strawberries, grapes, and apples. After that, pat them dry.

2. Slice the apples and chop them into bite-sized chunks.

3. Then, take the strawberries and slice them as well.

4. Mix the following ingredients together – yogurt, dried cranberries, pineapple, Mandarin oranges, grapes, and apples.

5. Keep the mixture covered and put it in the refrigerator for two hours.

6. Before serving, garnish the preparation with sliced strawberries.

Beet and Apple Juice Blend

Total Prep & Cooking Time: 5 minutes

Yields: 2 servings

Nutrition Facts: Calories: 53 | Carbs: 13g | Protein: 1g | Fat: 0g | Sodium: 66mg

Ingredients:

- A quarter cup of parsley
- Half a beet (medium-sized)
- Half an apple (medium-sized)
- One carrot (fresh, medium-sized)
- One stalk of celery

Method:

1. Process the following ingredients together in a juicer – parsley, celery, carrot, beet, and apple.

2. Take the mixture and pour it into two small glasses. You can either keep the juice in the refrigerator to chill or have it right away.

Notes: *Even though juices are healthy, for kidney patients, you have to be careful so that you don't increase your potassium intake too much.*

Baked Turkey Spring Rolls

Total Prep & Cooking Time: 1 hour 30 minutes

Yields: 8 servings (per serving – 2 spring rolls)

Nutrition Facts: Calories: 197 | Carbs: 9.6g | Protein: 23.3g | Fat: 7.3g | Sodium: 82.2mg

Ingredients:

- 2.5 cups of coleslaw mix
- Two tsps. of freshly ground black pepper
- Twenty ounces of turkey breast (ground)
- Two tbsps. each of
  - Vegetable oil
  - Minced cilantro
- One tbsp. each of
  - Sesame oil
  - Balsamic vinegar
- Two tsps. of freshly ground black pepper
- Sixteen pastry wrappers (frozen spring roll wraps)
- Cooking spray

Method:

1. Set the temperature of the oven to 400 degrees F and preheat.

2. Take the spring roll wrappers out from the freezer so that they can stay under room temperature. Thawing should be done at least half an hour before preparation.

3. Now, take a bowl, and in it, mix the following ingredients with the raw turkey – minced cilantro, sesame oil, and balsamic vinegar.

4. Take a large-sized skillet, and in it, pour two tbsps. of vegetable oil. Put the skillet on medium-high flame and preheat. Add the ground turkey

into the skillet and crumble it by stirring. To cook the turkey properly, you have to keep sautéing the mixture.

5. Then, you have to add the mixture of coleslaw to the turkey and keep cooking for another five minutes. Season with freshly ground black pepper – two tsps. should be enough. Mix everything properly.

6. Once done, remove the skillet from the flame. Use a strainer to drain any remaining liquid.

7. Take one spring roll wrapper and near one corner of it – add the filling diagonally. You can take three tbsps. of filling for one roll. There should be adequate space left on both sides. Fold one side towards the inside and do the same with the other side. Roll them and make sure the sights have been tucked in properly. Use water to moisten one of the sides of the wrapper because this helps to seal properly.

8. Take the remaining wrappers and follow the same steps with them.

9. Use non-stick cooking spray to coat the baking pan's base and then place the spring rolls in it. Place the pan in the oven, and it should be complete in half an hour when given at 400 degrees F.

10. You can also serve the rolls with a sweet chili sauce, but this has not been included in the nutrition facts.

Crab-Stuffed Celery Logs

Total Prep & Cooking Time: 10 minutes

Yields: 4 servings

Nutrition Facts: Calories: 34 | Carbs: 2g | Protein: 2g | Fat: 2g | Sodium: 94mg

Ingredients:

- Two tsps. of mayonnaise
- One tbsp. of red onion
- A quarter cup of crab meat
- Four ribs or celery (approx. eight inches in size)
- A quarter tsp. of paprika
- Half a tsp. of lemon juice

Method:

1. Take the celery ribs and trim the ends. Prepare the crab meat by draining it and then use two forks to flake the meat. Chop the onion and mince it thoroughly.

2. Take a small-sized bowl and in it, add the lemon juice, mayonnaise, onion, and crab meat and combine them properly.

3. Take a whole tablespoon full of the mixture and fill the celery rib with it.

4. Each rib of celery has to be cut into three equal pieces.

5. Sprinkle some paprika on top of each of these celery logs.

Couscous Salad

Total Prep & Cooking Time: 50 minutes

Yields: 4 servings (half a cup per serving)

Nutrition Facts: Calories: 151 | Carbs: 28.7g | Protein: 4.9g | Fat: 2.5g | Sodium: 14.3mg

Ingredients:

- One teaspoon each of
  - o Dried oregano
  - o Allspice
- Two lemons (juiced)
- One tbsp. each of
  - o Olive oil
  - o Minced garlic
- Half a cup each of
  - o Red bell pepper (chopped)
  - o Yellow bell pepper (chopped)
  - o Carrots (chopped)
  - o Frozen corn
- One cup each of
  - o Dry couscous
  - o Whole sugar snap peas
- Three peeled cucumbers (large-sized)

Method:

1. Follow the package instructions to prepare the couscous. After that, allow it to chill.

2. Take a large bowl and mix the following ingredients: cucumbers, couscous, snow peas, carrots, corn, yellow pepper, and red pepper.

3. Take another bowl of small size and, in it, whisk the following ingredients together – dried oregano, allspice, lemon juice, olive oil, and minced garlic.

4. Combine everything and serve it chilled.

Chapter 3: One-Week Meal Plan

Day 1

Breakfast – Pumpkin Pancakes

Lunch – Ground Beef Soup

Snacks – Frosted Grapes

Dinner – Pasta Salad

Day 2

Breakfast – Yogurt and Fruit Salad

Lunch – Broccoli and Apple Salad

Snacks – Apple Puffs

Dinner – Baked Turkey Spring Rolls

Day 3

Breakfast – Egg Muffins

Lunch – Minestrone Soup

Snacks – Crab-Stuffed Celery Logs

Dinner – Hawaiian Chicken Salad Sandwich

Day 4

Breakfast – Yogurt and Fruit Salad

Lunch – Pasta Salad

Snacks – Apple Puffs

Dinner – Linguine with Broccoli, Chickpeas, and Ricotta

Day 5

Breakfast – Beet and Apple Juice Blend

Lunch – Ground Beef Soup

Snacks – Frosted Grapes

Dinner – Baked Turkey Spring Rolls

Day 6

Breakfast – Pumpkin Pancakes

Lunch – Creamy Orzo and Vegetables

Snacks – Pineapple Frangelico Sorbet

Dinner – Couscous Salad

Day 7

Breakfast – Egg Muffins

Lunch – Broccoli and Apple Salad

Snacks – Pineapple Frangelico Sorbet

Dinner – Ground Beef Soup

Chapter 4: Avoiding Dialysis and Taking the Right Supplements

Even though getting diagnosed with chronic kidney disease (CKD) might appear scary, you can take certain steps to prolong your kidney function and delay the onset of dialysis if you catch the disease in its early stages. Some of the main causes of CKD in Americans are high blood pressure and diabetes. In order to prolong kidney function, these diseases should be controlled.

Steps to Avoid Dialysis and Prolong Kidney Function

There are steps an individual could take to prolong kidney function regardless of how the individual developed CKD.

- **Following a renal diet** – The main aim of a pre-dialysis diet is to maintain optimum nutrition. A renal diet is one that has a low content of protein, phosphorus, and sodium and emphasizes the importance of limiting the intake of fluids and consuming high-quality protein. It's essential to consult your dietician for individualized nutrition counseling. Several doctors believe that the progression of kidney diseases can be slowed down by following a renal diet.

- **Reduce the intake of salt** – Consuming an excess amount of salt with your foods is linked with high blood pressure.

- **Exercise regularly** – Exercises like running, walking, and swimming can help maintain a healthy weight, manage diabetes and high blood pressure, and decrease stress.

- **Reduce stress** – Decreasing stress and anxiety can lower your blood pressure, which in turn can be beneficial for your kidneys.

- **Don't smoke** – Smoking decreases the flow of blood to your kidneys. It decreases kidney function in both people with or without diseases.

- **Limit alcohol intake** – Alcohol consumption can increase your blood pressure. The excess calories can also make you gain weight.

- **Drink enough water** – Your kidneys can be damaged by dehydration, decreasing blood flow to the kidneys. However, follow your nutritionist's guidelines regarding fluid intake because regular fluid intake can also increase the build-up of fluid in your body, which can become dangerous for patients in the later stages of CKD.

- **Control your blood pressure** – High blood pressure can increase your risk of kidney failure and heart diseases.

- **Control your blood sugar** – The risk of kidney failure and heart diseases are increased due to diabetes.

- **Maintain a healthy weight** – The risk of kidney-related conditions like high blood pressure and diabetes can be increased because of obesity.

Even though CKD cannot be reversed, appropriate treatment can slow down its progression. See your doctor regularly to monitor your kidney function and slow the progression of kidney failure.

Supplements to Look Out for

The dietary requirements of people who are suffering from any sort of kidney problems are not always the same. Someone might need extra calories and proteins, whereas others might need fewer amounts of such nutrients. Thus, a professional healthcare provider is the best person who can assist and guide you for choosing the perfect supplements necessary for your kidney disease. Special supplements meant for keeping the kidney safe are available in various sizes, shapes, flavors, and forms. It is always necessary to consult a healthcare practitioner before consuming any nutritional supplement related to the kidney.

Individuals who are suffering from chronic kidney disease (CKD) require certain water-soluble vitamins in higher quantities. Here you will get to know about some of the supplements that are meant for dealing with kidney problems.

- **Vitamin B1 or Thiamin -** It looks after the proper functioning of the nervous system. Thiamin also helps the cells in producing the required amount of energy from carbohydrates. People with chronic kidney disease are recommended to intake 1.5mg of this water-soluble vitamin supplement per day.

- **Vitamin B2 or Riboflavin -** Vitamin B2 supports healthy skin as well as normal vision. People who are fighting against CKD and are also following a special low-protein diet might consume 1.8mg of Riboflavin supplement each day. Those of you who have a low appetite and are pursuing dialysis might take 1.1 to 1.3mg of vitamin B2 supplements per day.

- **Vitamin B6 -** This effective water-soluble vitamin helps produce proteins that are further used for making cells. Patients of CKD who are under dialysis treatment might consume 10mg of this supplement each day. Those who are non-dialysis patients are recommended to intake 5mg vitamin B6 supplements every day.

- **NAC -** NAC or N-acetylcysteine is an essential amino acid that generally targets the oxygen radicals. Various findings and researches suggest that NAC supplementation is beneficial for hemodialysis patients. NAC supplement decreases oxidative stress as well as improves results of uremic anemia, which is a problem of CKD.

- **ALA -** The antioxidant Alpha lipoic acid might prove helpful in treating certain complications of kidney disease. Supplementation of ALA enhances the action of a few antioxidant enzymes. Such enzymes protect against oxidative disorders and stress.

- **Vitamin B12 -** Vitamin B12 maintains the nerve cells and, in association with folate, produces red blood cells. Both dialysis and non-dialysis CKD patients are recommended to intake 2-3 mg of this supplement per day. Its deficiency can result in permanent nerve damage.

Supplements for kidney problems are better to consume only if it is approved or prescribed by your doctor.

PART IV

This chapter will give you a brief introduction to what the Hashimoto disease is and what diet you can follow in this case.

Chapter 1: Causes and Symptoms of Hashimoto Disease

Hashimoto's disease is a type of autoimmune disorder. It may lead to hypothyroidism (i.e., underactive thyroid). When you have this disease, your thyroid gets attacked by your immune system. It causes immense damage to the thyroid gland as a result of which it fails to produce an adequate amount of thyroid hormones. Hashimoto's disease causes inflammation (chronic lymphocytic thyroiditis), which eventually leads to hypothyroidism. Men and women of all ages and even children can get affected by this disease. Middle-aged women are more likely to get affected by this particular disease. Generally, a thyroid function test is suggested by the doctors for the detection of Hashimoto's disease. This disease can be treated by a simple thyroid hormone replacement effectively.

A study stated that earlier, it was a little difficult for the doctors to detect Hashimoto's disease. But now it can be easily identified by an antibody test (since this disease causes the production of harmful antibodies) and a hormone test (during hypothyroidism, the thyroid hormone level is low, whereas the level of TSH is more). The pituitary glands release more TSH so that it can stimulate the thyroid to increase the production of the thyroid hormone.

- People who get exposed to enormous amounts of radiation are more likely to develop Hashimoto's disease.

- Having an underlying medical condition often acts as a triggering factor in the case of developing new health issues. If you already have an autoimmune disease like type-1 diabetes or rheumatoid arthritis, then you are more prone to Hashimoto's disease.

- Heredity is an important factor when it comes to autoimmune diseases. So, if there is Hashimoto's disease in your family history, then you have a fair chance of developing the same.

- People of all ages can get affected by Hashimoto's disease, but middle-aged people are at higher risk.

- Gender is also a factor as women are more prone to this particular disease.

Hashimoto's disease can be asymptomatic at the beginning, but it slowly starts showing you symptoms after a few days. Let's see some of the symptoms of this disease.

- Memory lapse

- Depression

- Heavy menstrual bleeding (can also be prolonged)

- Muscle fatigue

- Pain in the joints and stiffness

- Muscle aches, stiffness, and tenderness

- Uncontrollable weight gain

- Tongue enlargement

- Loss of hair

- Nails become brittle

- The face becomes puffed up

- Dry and pale skin

- Constipation

- Hypersensitivity to cold

- Sluggishness and fatigue

Millions of individuals are surviving in this world who is suffering from Hashimoto's Disease or Hashimoto thyroiditis. This deep-rooted autoimmune situation makes the thyroid gland inactive. It is true that Hashimoto Disease develops or progresses slowly. But, such autoimmune condition attacks as well as destroys the thyroid gland. The symptoms of this disease might remain unnoticed for many years. Treatment begins after checking levels of one-two antibodies, namely thyroglobulin (Tg) and thyroperoxidase (TPO). In certain cases, the thyroid gland might also be checked through ultrasound. But, you need not worry as you may survive well even with this disease. Besides medical intervention, various supplements are available that play a crucial role in dealing with Hashimoto Disease.

But, before consuming any such supplements, it is better to consult your healthcare provider or practitioner. He or she is the perfect person who will be able to guide you according to your health condition. Here you will get to know about some of the essential supplements that you may consume for Hashimoto Disease.

- **Selenium**- Selenium assists the thyroid gland in producing thyroid hormone. It is also helpful in converting T4 (thyroxine) into T3 (triiodothyronine). Various studies have revealed the fact that selenium supplementation is effective for treating this disease, whether combined with levothyroxine or used alone. Selenium supplements are beneficial, but it is better not to

121

consume more than one hundred micrograms (mcg) each day. You may intake more or less than the mentioned quantity only if your doctor prescribes you to do so. For more trust-worthy selenium consumption, it is better to rely on supplements than food sources.

- **Zinc**- In accordance with certain reliable research, supplementation of zinc might help maintain a healthy thyroid hormone level. Expert healthcare providers usually suggest fifteen to thirty mg of zinc supplement daily. Zinc and selenium together are worthy of improving the functioning of the thyroid.

- **Omega-3 Fatty Acid**- It is believed that omega-3 fatty acids, particularly docosahexaenoic acid (DHA) and icosapentaenoic acid (EPA) are helpful for individual suffering from autoimmune thyroid conditions. It is recommended to consume fish oil supplements twice or thrice a week. Omega-3 fatty acid supplement (plant-based) is also beneficial but is not so well absorbed like fish oil supplements.

- **Vitamin B1**- Evidence exists that thiamine or vitamin B1 supplements are useful in reducing fatigue of those people having Hashimoto's thyroiditis. This disease leads to decreased thiamine absorption. If you are facing such a problem, you may discuss it with your physician for the dosage of thiamine supplementation.

Chapter 2: Recipes for Appetizers and Snacks

Oven Roasted Okra

Total Prep & Cooking Time: 35 minutes

Yields: Four servings

Nutrition Facts: Calories: 104 | Carbs: 9.4g | Protein: 2.2g | Fat: 7.2g | Fiber: 3.6g

Ingredients:

- One pound of okra
- One tbsp. each of
  - Lemon juice
  - Balsamic vinegar
- One teaspoon each of
  - Onion powder
  - Garlic powder
- A quarter teaspoon of black pepper
- Two tablespoons of avocado oil
- A three-fourth teaspoon of sea salt

Method:

1. Set the oven temperature at 400 degrees F. You will require a baking sheet to bake the okra. With a parchment paper, line the sheet.

2. Rinse the okras thoroughly under running water and dry them. Chop off the head of each okra. Slice each okra into five pieces and then set them aside.

3. Place the okra pieces evenly on the sheet and top them with salt, pepper, lemon, oil, and balsamic vinegar. Toss them well so that the okra is entirely coated with the seasonings.

4. Transfer the sheet to an oven and roast them for twenty-four to twenty-five minutes. Flip the pieces in between to cook both sides evenly.

5. Take the sheet off the oven and then allow them to cool down.

6. Serve and enjoy.

Note: *Okra is an incredibly delicious summer vegetable.*

Honeydew Smoothie Bowl

Total Prep & Cooking Time: 5 minutes

Yields: 2 servings

Nutrition Facts: Calories: 176 | Carbs: 41.4g | Protein: 2.5g | Fat: 1.6g | Fiber: 3g

Ingredients:

- One tbsp. of honey
- One-third cup of green juice of your choice (for example, wheatgrass)
- Half a cup of coconut milk beverage (unsweetened)
- Four cups of cubed honeydew (frozen, make pieces of half an inch in size)
- Salt as per taste
- For garnishing – nuts, fresh basil, berries, and melon balls

Method:

1. Use a high-speed blender or food processor to blend the following ingredients together – salt, honey, juice, coconut milk, and honeydew. Stop in between blending and pulsing to scrape down the sides of the food processor.

2. Pulse for about one to two minutes to get your desired consistency. Before serving, top the smoothie with toppings of your choice.

Wake-Up Smoothie

Total Prep & Cooking Time: 5 minutes

Yields: 3 servings

Nutrition Facts: Calories: 139 | Carbs: 28g | Protein: 4.4g | Fat: 2g | Fiber: 4.3g

Ingredients:

- One banana
- 1.25 cups of orange juice (if possible, then calcium-fortified)
- Half a cup of silken tofu (low-fat) or low-fat yogurt
- 1.25 cups of frozen berries such as blackberries, raspberries, strawberries, or blueberries
- One tbsp. of sugar or Stevia

Method:

1. In the bowl of a blender, add the ingredients.
2. Cover the bowl and blend the ingredients until you get a smooth and creamy mixture.
3. Serve and enjoy!

Cucumber Radish Salsa

Total Prep Time: 10 minutes

Yields: Four plates of salsa

Nutrition Facts: Calories: 22 | Carb: 4.7g | Protein: 0.9g | Fat: 0.4g | Fiber: 1.6g

Ingredients:

- One large-sized cucumber (sliced)
- A quarter cup of chopped cilantro
- Two juiced limes
- One heaping cup of radishes, eight to ten regular (either sliced into thin halves or diced)
- Three tablespoons of diced red onion
- One tablespoon of olive oil
- To taste: Pepper (freshly ground and optional) and salt

Method:

1. In a bowl, place all the veggies listed in the ingredients section.

2. Combine them thoroughly, and place them in a refrigerator for one hour before serving.

Crispy Oven-Fried Fish Tacos

Total Prep & Cooking Time: 45 minutes

Yields: 4 servings (Two tacos per serving)

Nutrition Facts: Calories: 496 | Carbs: 65.4g | Protein: 27.3g | Fat: 17.6g | Fiber: 15.2g

Ingredients:

- A cup of cereal flakes (whole-grain)
- Cooking spray
- Half a tsp. each of
  - o   Salt (keep it divided)
  - o   Paprika
  - o   Garlic powder
- Half a cup of all-purpose flour
- Three-quarter tsp. of freshly ground pepper (keep it divided)
- Three-quarter cups of breadcrumbs (whole wheat)
- Two egg whites
- One lb. of cod (cut into strips)
- Two tbsps. each of
  - o   Avocado oil
  - o   Water
  - o   Unseasoned rice vinegar
- One avocado (sliced)
- Pico de gallo
- Three cups of coleslaw mix
- Eight warmed corn tortillas

Method:

1. Set the temperature of the oven to 450 degrees F and preheat. Take a baking sheet and, on it, place a wire rack. Use cooking spray to coat it nicely.

2. In the bowl of a food processor, add the breadcrumbs, cereal flakes, paprika, garlic powder, half a tsp. of pepper, and half a tsp. of salt. Process all these ingredients until you get a smooth mixture. Take this mixture and spread it on a shallow dish.

3. Take another shallow dish and place flour on it. Then, in the third shallow dish, whisk water and egg together.

4. Take each fillet of fish, dredge it in flour, and then dip the fillet in the egg mixture. Then, coat both sides of the fillets with breadcrumbs evenly.

5. Once done, place these fillets on the greased wire racks. The breaded fish should be coated with cooking spray as well. Bake them for about ten minutes by the end of which they should become golden brown and crispy.

6. Meanwhile, take a medium-sized bowl and, in it, whisk the following ingredients together – remaining pepper and salt, vinegar, and oil. Add the mix of coleslaw to it and toss nicely so that everything is evenly coated.

7. Finally, take the tortillas, divide the avocados, coleslaw mix, and fish evenly. If you want, then serve them with pico de gallo.

Strawberry Mango Salsa

Total Prep Time: 10 minutes

Yields: Four servings

Nutrition Facts: Calories: 126 | Carbs: 20.3g | Protein: 1.8g | Fat: 5.7g | Fiber: 4.6g

Ingredients:

- One cup of diced strawberries
- A quarter cup of diced red onions
- A tablespoon of chopped cilantro
- One medium-sized mango (chopped)
- One medium avocado (sliced)
- One lime, juiced
- To taste: Salt

Method:

1. In a bowl (medium-sized), add all ingredients listed in the section, except the salt. Carefully combine them with spatula's help so that the veggies get well coated with the lime juice. Make sure that you do not crush the avocado pieces.

2. After the ingredients have been entirely tossed, sprinkle over the salt. You can serve immediately, or you can store in the refrigerator in a closed container.

Strawberry Mousse

Total Prep & Cooking Time: 6 hours and 30 minutes

Yields: Six servings

Nutrition Facts: Calories: 100 | Carbs: 20g | Protein: 5g | Fat: 0g | Fiber: 1g

Ingredients:

- Twelve ounces of halved and hulled fresh strawberries
- A three-fourth cup of Greek yogurt
- Lemon juice (few drops)
- One-third cup of honey
- Four egg whites
- Salt to taste

Method:

1. Place strawberries and honey in a blender and make them smooth. Put them in a bowl.

2. Pour the yogurt in the bowl and whisk them properly.

3. Take another bowl. Add the lemon splash, salt, and egg whites. Using a hand mixer, whisk the eggs to form stiff peaks such a way that the egg remains intact when turned upside down.

4. With a spatula, mix one-third of the egg mixture with strawberry. Slowly pour the rest of the egg whites mixture, ensuring that the bubbles do not break.

5. Transfer to six containers. Store the containers for six hours in the refrigerator. Enjoy.

Grilled Salmon and Veggies

Total Prep & Cooking Time: 25 minutes

Yields: Four servings

Nutrition Facts: Calories: 281 | Carbs: 10.6g | Protein: 30.2g | Fat: 2.3g | Fiber: 3.1g

Ingredients:

- One medium-sized zucchini, sliced vertically into halves
- One onion (cut into wedges of one-inch), red

- Half a tsp. of salt
- One and a quarter lb. of salmon fillets (sliced into portions of four)
- One lemon, sliced into wedges of four
- Two bell peppers (each of red, orange, yellow), halved, seeded, and trimmed
- One tbsp. of olive oil (extra-virgin)
- Half a tsp. of pepper (ground)
- A quarter cup of fresh basil (thinly sliced)

Method:

1. Keep the grill preheated to moderate heat.

2. Place onions, pepper, and zucchini in a bowl sprinkle some salt (a quarter tsp.) and brush them with oil.

3. Place the salmon fillets in another bowl and sprinkle with remaining salt and pepper.

4. Transfer the salmon and the veggies to grill and then cook the vegetables occasionally, turning and cooking each side for six minutes until they tenderize. Cook the salmon for ten minutes until they flake.

5. Remove the vegetables and chop them into small pieces when they have cooled down. Toss them well. Serve the salmon aside the vegetables. Garnish them with one tbsp. of basil and the lemon wedges.

Chapter 3: Main Course Recipes

Zucchini Noodles With Shrimp and Avocado Pesto

Total Prep & Cooking Time: 35 minutes

Yields: 4 servings (1.75 cups each serving)

Nutrition Facts: Calories: 446 | Carbs: 15.8g | Protein: 25.9g | Fat: 33.2g | Fiber: 6.6g

Ingredients:

- One avocado (ripe)
- One cup of basil leaves (fresh)
- Three-quarter tsp. of salt (keep it divided)
- Five-six zucchini (medium-sized, trimmed)
- A quarter cup of pistachios (shelled, unsalted)
- Three garlic cloves (minced)
- A quarter cup of olive oil (extra-virgin variety, + two tbsps. extra)
- A quarter tsp. of freshly ground pepper
- 1-2 tsps. of Old Bay seasoning
- One lb. of raw shrimp (deveined and peeled)
- Two tbsps. of lemon juice

Method:

1. Your first step is to prepare the zucchini using a spiralizer and form thin strips. Then, take the zoodles and place them in a colander. Sprinkle half a tsp. of salt. Allow it to drain for half an hour and squeeze to remove any excess water.

2. In a food processor, combine the following – pepper, lemon juice, pistachios basil, avocado, and a quarter tsp. of salt. Make sure everything is finely chopped. To make it smooth, add a quarter cup of oil.

3. In a large-sized skillet, heat one tbsp. of oil on medium-high flame. Cook the garlic in the heated oil for about thirty seconds. Then, sprinkle the Old Bay seasoning and add the shrimp. Keep stirring and cook the shrimp for about four minutes. Once done, transfer the shrimp to a bowl.

4. Take the remaining one tbsp. of oil and add it to the pan. The zoodles should have drained by now, so you have to add them to the pan and toss them for about three minutes. Then, transfer them to the bowl containing shrimp and mix properly. Add the pesto and combine it by tossing everything once again. Serve and enjoy!

Honey Ginger Shrimp Bowls

Total Prep & cooking Time: 26 minutes

Yields: Two bowls

Nutrition Facts: Calories: 165.9 | Carbs: 4.1g | Protein: 19g | Fat: 8.1g | Fiber: 0.8g

Ingredients:

For preparing the shrimp,

- Twelve ounces of large deveined and peeled shrimp (uncooked)
- One teaspoon of freshly minced ginger
- Two teaspoons of avocado oil
- Two tablespoons each of
  o Honey
  o Coconut aminos
- Two cloves of garlic (diced)
- To taste: salt, lime, pepper (ground freshly, optional)

Dressing ingredients,

- Two tablespoons each of
  o Olive oil
  o Lime juice
- A quarter teaspoon each of

- o   Ginger powder
- o   Garlic powder
- One teaspoon each of
  - o   Coconut aminos
  - o   Honey
- To taste – Pepper and salt

Salad ingredients,

- Four cups of spinach or arugula
- Four onions sliced (green)
- One avocado (diced)
- Half a cup each of
  - o   Carrots (shredded)
  - o   Radishes (shredded)
- A quarter of cilantro (sliced)

Method:

1. Take a bowl and put coconut aminos, ginger, honey, and garlic. Combine them well with a whisk.

2. Take a lidded container and pour the shrimp into it along with the marinade. Stir thoroughly.

3. Marinate the shrimp for two hours in the refrigerator.

4. After the period described above, pour some avocado oil in the skillet and heat over moderate flame. Pour the shrimp mixture into the skillet. Cook for about three minutes to make the shrimp opaque and then flip.

5. Continue cooking for an additional three minutes to make the sauce thickened—season with lime, pepper, and salt. Cook well to form an even coating over the shrimp pieces.

6. Toss carrots, greens, and radishes in a bowl and then divide equally into two plates.

7. To serve: top each dish with the cooked shrimp, cilantro, avocado, dressing, onions, and wedges.

Note: You can chop the carrots and radishes with shredding attachment or the box grater. Be careful while cooking the shrimp. The inner flesh must be white, and the outer tissue should turn pink.

Beef and Sweet Potatoes Stew

Total Prep & Cooking Time: 20 minutes

Yields: Four servings

Nutrition Facts: Calories: 195 | Carbs: 18g | Protein: 19g | Fat: 5g | Fiber: 3g

Ingredients:

- One teaspoon each of
  o Avocado oil
  o Salt
- One tablespoon of minced ginger
- Two teaspoons each of
  o Oregano (dried)
  o Thyme (dried)
- One cup each of
  o Pumpkin puree
  o Cilantro (chopped)
  o Carrots (sliced)
- One pound of grass-fed beef (ground)
- Diced avocado
- One diced onion
- Three cloves of garlic (minced)
- Five cups of cubed and peeled sweet potato
- Two cups bone broth
- Two limes juiced
- Six sliced green onions
- Pepper to taste and optional

Method

1. Pour avocado oil in an instant pot and set the function to 'saute.' After oil starts to boil, add the ginger, carrots, onion, garlic, sweet potatoes, thyme, pepper, salt, and oregano, stir for few minutes until you get the smell.

2. Turn it off. Add the bone broth and the pumpkin puree to the mixture and beef (ground) to form a single layer at the bottom.

3. Cook the stew using the manual setting for five minutes. Release the method by switching to the quick-release mode.

4. Season with lime juice. Divide equally among four bowls and top with avocado and herbs to serve.

Roasted Sunchoke Salad

Total Prep & Cooking Time: 35 minutes

Yields: Four servings

Nutrition Facts: Calories: 143 | Carbs: 20g | Protein: 2g | Fat: 6g | Fiber: 2g

Ingredients:

- Two pounds of trimmed and scrubbed sunchokes
- Half a cup of minced red onion
- Two tablespoons of avocado oil
- A three-fourth cup of parsley (minced)
- One clove of garlic (diced)
- To taste: Black pepper (ground) and salt

Method:

1. Set the oven at a temperature of 425 degrees F. place a baking sheet on your countertop. Mix the sunchokes, pepper, salt, and one tbsp. of avocado oil. Toss them well over the baking sheet in an even layer.

2. Bake for thirty minutes, occasionally stirring until the edges turn brown and crispy, leaving the middle portions creamy.

3. Meanwhile, in a bowl, place the remaining ingredients and then add the sunchokes mixture. Stir them well and add some seasoning if required.

4. Serve immediately.

Kale Salad

Total Prep Time: 20 minutes

Yields: Four bowls of salad

Nutrition Facts: Calories: 334 | Carbs: 19g | Protein: 9g | Fat: 26g | Fiber: 4g

Ingredients:

- Five cups of chopped kale
- One-eighth tsp. of salt
- Half a cup each of
  - Cheese
  - Sliced almonds
- A quarter cup each of
  - Seeds of sunflower
  - Cranberries
  - Diced red onions
- Two tsps. of olive oil
- Two cups of chopped broccoli
- A quarter to a half cup of shredded carrots

For the lemon dressing,

- A quarter cup of oil (olive)
- One tbsp. of Dijon mustard
- Half a tsp. of oregano (dried)

- One-eighth tsp. of black pepper (ground)
- Two tbsps. each of
  - Lemon juice
  - Vinegar (red wine)
- One garlic clove (minced)
- A quarter tsp. of salt
- One tsp. of sugar or honey

Method:

1. Massage the chopped kale leaves with salt and oil. Brush them with the fingers to make the leaves become tender and darken in color.

2. For the dressing, mix all ingredients in the jar with a lid. Shake them well so that they emulsify. Adjust the sweetener, pepper, and salt as your heart desires.

3. Take a bowl and place broccoli, massaged kale, cheese, onion, almond, carrots, cranberries, and sunflower seeds. Toss them well. Pour the dressing ingredients over it (about one-third). Shake well to coat and then add the extra dressing according to your taste.

Taco Spaghetti Squash Boats

Total Prep & Cooking Time: 45 minutes

Yields: Four servings

Nutrition Facts: Calories: 553 | Carbs: 28g | Protein: 29.6g | Fat: 38.5g | Fiber: 9g

Ingredients:

- Two tbsps. of canola oil
- One cup each of
    o   Onion (chopped)
    o   Blended and shredded cheese (Mexican)
    o   Chopped lettuce (romaine)
- One medium-sized tomato (diced)
- Two tsps. of cumin (ground)
- A quarter cup of prepared salsa (some extra for serving)
- One chopped avocado
- Three lb. of spaghetti squash, seeded and vertically sliced into halves
- Half a tsp. of salt
- Four tsps. of chili powder
- Three garlic (diced)
- One lb. of turkey (ground)

Method:

1. Set the oven at a temperature of 450 degrees F. Place a skillet over moderate flame and pour few oil drops. Then add the garlic, onion, and turkey. Cook for seven minutes, stirring occasionally and breaking the turkey chunks. Then add chili powder, salt, tomato, and cumin. Cook thoroughly for three minutes. Stir in the salsa after removing from heat.

2. Take a microwave-safe dish and place the cut-side down of squash on it. Add two tbsps. of water to the squash. Place the dish (uncovered) inside the microwave and bake for fifteen minutes. Make sure the squash flesh becomes tender.

3. Scrape out the flesh of squash from its shells with a fork. While the turkey mixture is still in the skillet, add the scooped squash flesh to it. Sprinkle remaining salt and then stir well.

4. Take a sheet (baking) and then arrange the squash shells on it. Scoop back the squash mixture into the shells. Top them with cheese. Thoroughly bake for fifteen minutes. Wait until the cheese melts and then top with avocado and lettuce. Serve with extra salsa if desired and enjoy.

Lemon Asparagus Chicken Skillet

Total Prep & Cooking Time: 35 minutes

Yields: Three plates

Nutrition Facts: Calories: 335 | Carbs: 14g | Protein: 36.9g | Fat: 15g | Fiber: 1.6g

Ingredients:

- Two tablespoons of avocado oil
- Half a teaspoon pepper
- One bunch of asparagus
- One-third cup of chicken broth
- One tablespoon of coconut aminos
- One teaspoon each of
  - Salt
  - Arrowroot starch
- One pound of chicken breast, sliced into cubes
- Three garlic cloves, minced
- One lemon juiced

Method:

1. Pour the avocado oil in the skillet and heat it over moderate heat.

2. After the oil starts to bubble out, add the chicken cubes and season with pepper and salt. Cook until the chicken becomes tender (insert the thermometer into the chicken's thickest part and check if it reads a

temperature of 165 degrees F) and then remove the chicken and set it aside.

3.   To prepare the asparagus, chop off its thick white base and cut them vertically into halves.

4.   Saute the asparagus for seven minutes with more pepper, oil, and salt if needed. They should become soft with a little crisp. Set them aside.

5.   Lower the flame and then add the garlic to the skillet. Cook until it gives out the fragrance.

6.   One by one, add the arrowroot starch, lemon juice, broth, and the coconut aminos. Stir them for about three minutes until the sauce attains a thickened consistency.

7.   Add the asparagus and chicken pieces to the skillet and cook thoroughly for three more minutes.

8.   Remove from the heat and top with onion wedges. Season more to satisfy your taste and finally serve it warm.

Note: *This is an allergen-friendly meal that is made with foods that can provide you with the best of protein source and lime that is there to give a touch of acidic flavor. Chicken breast is good-to-go with this dish as it is easy to cook and makes things go smoother. You can omit the pepper part if you are on an AIP diet. Chicken broth is there to add the desired flavor and save the dish from getting thickened.*

Egg Roll in a Bowl

Total Prep & Cooking Time: 30 minutes

Yields: Four servings

Nutrition Facts: Calories: 351 | Carbs: 15.8g | Protein: 38.2g | Fat: 15.8g | Fiber: 2.6g

Ingredients:

For preparing the roll,

- One pound of pork (ground)
- One diced onion (white)
- One teaspoon of ginger (grated)
- Two teaspoons of vinegar (apple cider)
- Two tablespoons each of
  o Chopped onion (green)
  o Sesame oil
- Two garlic cloves (diced)
- Twelve ounces of coleslaw mix
- Three tablespoons of coconut aminos

For preparing the sauce (optional),

- A quarter cup of coconut cream
- One teaspoon of vinegar (apple cider)

- Salt
- One tablespoon of coconut aminos
- Two teaspoons of freshly grated ginger

Method:

1. Take a large-sized skillet and cook the pork over moderate flame. Season with salt and pepper. Cook until the pork turns brown and then set it aside. You are recommended to dispose off the fat.

2. Pour some oil in the same skillet and heat over moderate flame. Once the oil starts to boil, add the ginger, garlic, and the onion to it. Cook to turn the onion translucent, and the garlic begins to give fragrance.

3. To the mixture, add the vinegar, coleslaw mix, and the coconut aminos—season with pepper and salt. Stir them properly for about five minutes.

4. Pour back the precooked pork to the skillet and then stir well. Saute the mixture for an additional minute.

5. Transfer the pork to the bowls. Top with the optional sauce and the onion. Serve and enjoy

For preparing the sauce,

1. Combine all ingredients for preparing the sauce and then stir well.

2. Serve the mixture over each bowl.

Note: *Coconut aminos is the substitute for the soy sauce. Avoid using a coleslaw mix that is too much filled with carrots to your dish extra sugary.*

One-pan Chicken Pesto

Total Prep & Cooking Time: 40 minutes

Yields: Three to Four plates of pesto

Nutrition Facts: Calories: 556 | Carbs: 24.5g | Protein: 43g | Fat: 32.5g | Fiber: 4.2g

Ingredients:

For preparing the sheet pan,

- Two pounds of chicken breast (you may substitute with chicken thigh), bone-in
- Two zucchinis (diced)
- One medium-sized red onion (finely chopped)
- Half a tsp. each of
  o Black pepper
  o Sea salt
- Two carrots (thinly sliced into circles)
- One sliced squash (yellow)

For preparing the mint basil pesto,

- One cup each of
  o Arugula
  o Basil (fresh)
- Two tablespoons of fresh mint
- A quarter cup of a freshly juiced lemon
- Half a tsp. of salt
- Half a cup of avocado oil
- One garlic clove (minced and peeled)

Method:

1. Add the ingredients for preparing the pesto into the blender and then process it. Do not turn the blender off until the mixture gets combined thoroughly. After you are done, set the mixture aside.

2. Set the oven at a temperature of 400 degrees F. you will require a baking sheet and a parchment paper. With the parchment paper, line the large-sized baking sheet.

3. Place all ingredients for preparing sheet pan on the sheet evenly. The ingredients must not be crowded. Coat the vegetables and the chicken properly with the pesto. Leave about two tablespoons of pesto for later use.

4. Place the baking sheet on the oven. After every ten minutes, flip the vegetables so that both sides are cooked evenly. Continue cooking for thirty-five minutes. After the said mark, insert a thermometer in the chicken's thickest part. If the reading shows 165 degrees F, then you may stop cooking. It means you have cooked the chicken thoroughly and have tenderized it.

5. Transfer the chicken to the plates. Top each plate with the leftover pesto and serve warm.

Note: An important part to note is that you should prevent overcrowding the pan in which you are cooking. The vegetables must be chopped with even thickness as it will ensure they finish cooking at the same time. The bone-in chicken is recommended as it leads to flavor enhancement and keeps the meat juicy.

BBQ Jackfruit

Total Prep & Cooking Time: 10 minutes

Yields: Two servings

Nutrition Facts: Calories: 471 | Carbs: 83.8g | Protein: 4.9g | Fat: 15.7g | Fiber: 4.7g

Ingredients:

- A can of jackfruit (fourteen ounces)
- Half a teaspoon of salt
- Two teaspoons each of
  - Onion powder
  - Garlic powder
  - Coconut sugar
- Two tablespoons each of
  - Avocado oil
  - Chopped green onion
- A quarter of black pepper
- One teaspoon of chili powder
- Half a cup of BBQ sauce

Method:

1. Remove the excess liquid from the jackfruit can.

2. Place a large-sized pan over a moderate flame. Then add jackfruit and sprinkle some salt, garlic, chili powder, coconut sugar, pepper, and onion. Stir well for three minutes until they soften.

3. Add the BBQ sauce to it and toss the veggies well to coat them with the sauce. Make the vegetables incorporated. Simmer for about three minutes.

4. Transfer the preparation to the plates. Top each plate with onions.

5. Serve warm and enjoy.

Chapter 4: How to Increase Immunity to Prevent Further Relapse?

If you're suffering from Hashimoto's, your thyroid gets inflamed because of the extra stress on your immune system, and as a result, the thyroid hormones are under-produced. You can prevent further relapses of Hashimoto disease and restore the optimal functions of your thyroid by increasing your immunity. You can boost your immunity and restore the function of your thyroid by using a few easy yet proven lifestyle and dietary changes (Premawardhana, 2006).

1. **Repair your gut** – It is essential to repair your gut if you have Hashimoto's. Almost eighty percent of your whole immune system is situated in your digestive system. The intestinal wall should be just a little permeable to allow the nutrients to reach the bloodstream. However, when it gets leaky, bigger molecules can enter your bloodstream and cause chronic inflammation. The immune system detects them as foreign invaders. Some of these invaders are very similar to the blood cells of the body, and so the immune system ends up attacking your thyroid accidentally. Thus, repairing the gut is extremely important. You can do it with the help of the amino acids and nutrients it requires and by eliminating inflammatory foods, parasites, infections, and toxins. You also need to re-inoculate with healthy bacteria and restore the acids and enzymes that are essential for proper digestion.

2. **Tame the toxins** – We are exposed to several hundreds of toxins in our daily lives. Toxins like nitrates, percolates, and mercury can accumulate in your body and impact your thyroid functions as they are chemically similar to iodine. You can, however, eliminate these toxins from your

155

body and prevent your exposure to them by taking a few necessary steps. Firstly, you need to learn how you are getting exposed to them and then try to minimize your exposure. After that, you can try detox pathways to flush the toxins safely from your body.

3. **Heal your infections** – Bacterial and viral infections can trigger Hashimoto's in various ways. Some common infections often don't show any symptoms. However, they can be tested for and treated.

4. **Relieve your stress** – Your adrenal gland produces and releases a large number of hormones when you're under stress. These signals make the stressor a priority and dismiss other functions, including the production of thyroid hormone and immune response. It can negatively affect your thyroid. Learning how to relieve stress can immensely help prevent the relapse of Hashimoto's. Walking, running, mediation, and deep breathing exercises can all help relieve stress and also prevent you from falling into a state of chronic stress.

PART V

Chapter 1: Tasty Breakfast Options

French Crepe

Servings Provided: 8

Time Required: 20 minutes

What is Needed:

The Crepes:

- Eggs (2)
- Melted butter (.25 cup)
- Sugar (2.5 tbsp.)
- A-P flour (.5 cup)

- Milk (.5 cup)

- Water (.125 cup)

- Vanilla (.5 tsp.)

- Dash (tiny dash)

  The Filling:

- Powdered sugar (2-4 tbsp./as desired)

- Heavy whipping cream (1 cup)

- Vanilla extract (.5 tsp.)

- Freshly sliced strawberries

- Also Needed: Non-stick - 6-inch skillet

Preparation Method:

1. Prepare the crepes. Whisk all the fixings except the flour.

2. Fold in the flour - a little bit at a time - whisking just until the flour is incorporated.

3. Let the crepe batter rest for ten minutes. Whisk again before using it.

4. Grease the skillet with unsalted butter and warm it using the medium-temperature setting.

5. Pour about two to three tablespoons of batter into the pan - while tipping the pan from side to side to get the mixture spreading over the pan.

6. Cook each side of the crepe for half a minute before gently loosening the edges with a large spatula. If it lifts, it's ready to be flipped. If not, cook it for another 10-15 seconds and try again. Gently lift the crepe out of the pan, then flip over into the pan and cook the other side for another 10-15 seconds; remove to cool.

7. Prepare the filling. Use a hand/stand mixer to beat the heavy whipping

cream until soft peaks form. Add in the powdered sugar and vanilla. Continue mixing until stiff peaks form.

8. Spread a layer of cream over each crepe, sliced strawberries, and roll the crepe as you would a wrap.

French Omelette

Servings Provided: 1

Time Required: 15 minutes

What is Needed:

- Milk (1 tbsp.)
- Egg (1)
- Basil (1 tbsp.)
- Chives (1 tbsp.)
- Tarragon (.5 tbsp.)
- Salt and pepper (a pinch of each)
- Olive oil (as needed for the pan)
- Sundried tomato (1 thinly sliced - oil drained)
- Crumbled goat cheese (1 tbsp.)

Preparation Method:

1. Chop the basil, tarragon, and chives.
2. Whisk the milk, egg, salt, and pepper in a small mixing container. Add

half of the fresh herbs and gently stir to combine.

3. Add one tablespoon of olive oil to a small pan. Warm the oil using medium heat as you swirl it around the pan so that it coats the entire bottom of the pan and a little bit along the sides of the pan.

4. Dump the egg mixture into the pan. Swirl the pan so that the egg batter goes to the edges of the pan. Use a rubber spatula to gently push the egg batter to the edges of the pan.

5. Once the egg batter looks set on the bottom and is starting to bubble up a bit, lift the pan while tilting it to one side to slide the egg onto an awaiting using a large spatula. Flip the egg onto its other side into the pan and place it back on the burner using low heat.

6. Toss the crumbled cheese and tomato slices into the center of the omelet. Gently fold one side of the egg over, folding one more time - over itself (into thirds).

7. Serve promptly, garnished with the remaining fresh herbs.

Chapter 2: Delicious Salads

Traditional French Country Salad With Lemon Dijon
Vinaigrette

Servings Provided: 4

Time Required: 20 minutes

What is Needed:

- Arugula (5 oz. bag)
- Asparagus (.5 lb.)
- Olive oil (as desired)
- Sea salt (as desired)
- Sliced cooked beets (.5 cup)
- Whole walnuts or pecans, toasted (.5 cup)
- Crumbled goat cheese (.25 cup)
  The Vinaigrette:

- Balsamic vinegar (3 tbsp.)
- Dijon mustard (2 tbsp.)
- Olive oil (2 tbsp.)
- Minced garlic cloves (2 small)
- Sea salt & black pepper(.5 tsp./to taste)
- Lemon & zest (half of 1 lemon)

Preparation Method:

1. Set the oven at 400° Fahrenheit. Prepare a baking tray with a piece of parchment baking paper.
2. Trim the tattered ends and cut the asparagus into 1.5-inch long pieces. Spread it onto the prepared baking sheet. Drizzle the olive oil over the asparagus along with a sprinkle of sea salt.
3. Roast the asparagus for four to five minutes or until the asparagus is tender but still has a bite. Let it cool.
4. Toss the arugula with the asparagus in a large bowl.
5. Prepare the dressing. Whisk all of the vinaigrette fixings in a small measuring cup.
6. Assemble the salad. Toss the salad with the vinaigrette until everything is lightly coated, and garnish it using sliced beets, toasted nuts, and

crumbled goat cheese.

Chapter 3: Soup

Classic French Onion Bistro Soup

Servings Provided: 4

Time Required: 1.5 hours

What is Needed:

- Onions, (8 cups sliced/2 extra-large)
- Unsalted butter (1.5 tbsp.)
- Oil (1 tbsp.)
- Salt (.5 tsp.)
- Sugar (1 pinch)
- A-P flour (1.5 tbsp.)
- Low-sodium beef broth (4 cups)

- Pepper & salt (as desired)
- Sliced crusty French bread
- Gruyere cheese for the top/gruyere-cheddar mix (4 oz.)
- Also Needed: Oven-proof bowls (4)

Preparation Method:

1. Melt the butter with oil over low heat in a large pot or dutch oven. Slice the onions into crescent shapes and toss them into the pan. Place a lid on the pan and simmer them for about 15 minutes.
2. Slice the bread into ½-inch slices and toast them (set aside).
3. Adjust the stovetop temperature setting slightly higher and stir in the salt and sugar. Simmer with the lid off for another 40 to 45 minutes until onions have caramelized. Stir them occasionally throughout the duration.
4. Sprinkle the flour into the pot, stir, and simmer an additional three minutes.
5. Slowly add the broth into the pot, stirring as your pour. Season with a pinch of salt and pepper and cook for another 20 minutes until simmering and hot.
6. Warm the oven at 350° Fahrenheit.
7. Once the soup is ready, divide the soup into bowls. Place four to five baguette slices into each bowl. Top each bowl with grated cheese (.25 cup each dish).
8. Bake them until the cheese completely melts and serve promptly.

Fresh French Pea Soup

Servings Provided: 4

Time Required: 17 minutes

What is Needed:

- Butter with salt (2 tbsp.)
- Shallots (2 medium)
- Water (2 cups)
- Fresh green peas (3 cups)
- Table salt (.25 tsp.)

- Heavy whipping cream (3 tbsp.)

Preparation Method:

1. Prepare a heavy-bottomed saucepan (medium temp) to melt the butter. Sauté the shallots until soft and translucent (3 min.).

2. Pour in the water, peas, pepper, and salt. Adjust the temperature setting to med-high and bring to a boil.

3. Once boiling, lower the temperature setting to low, cover, and simmer until the peas are tender (12-18 min.).

4. Puree the peas in a food processor/blender in batches. Strain the pureed peas back into the saucepan, stir in the cream, and warm until it's piping hot.

5. Season to your liking with pepper and salt before serving.

Green Vegetable Soup

Servings Provided: 6

Time Required: 1 hour 40 minutes

What is Needed:

- Onions (2)
- Garlic (3 cloves)
- Butter, with salt (3 tbsp.)
- Swanson Clear Chicken Broth CAM (2 - 14.5 oz. cans)

- Water (4.5 cups)

- Carrots (3)

- Leeks (1)

- Spring onions/scallions - include tops & bulb (3)

- Habanero pepper (1 ½)

- Spinach (10 oz. bag)

- Watercress (1 bunch - raw)

- Table salt (1 tbsp.)

- Extra-virgin olive oil NOI (.25 cup)

- Red wine vinegar (50 Grain) NAK (.125 cup)

Preparation Method:

1. Warm a skillet using the med-high temperature setting. Sauté the minced garlic and onion (5 min.).

2. Add the water, chicken stock, spinach, carrots, green onions, leeks, habanero peppers, and watercress. Prepare it using a low-boil until the carrots are softened (30 min.). Remove the pan from the burner, and cool it for about half an hour.

3. When cooled, puree the soup in a food processor until smooth. Pour the mixture into the pot, and simmer using the low-temperature setting for 15 minutes.

4. Serve with a drizzle of olive oil and vinegar to your liking.

Chapter 4: Beef Options

Beef Bourguignon - Slow-Cooked

Servings Provided: 6

Time Required: 2.5 hours

What is Needed:

- Bacon (6 oz. - diced)
- Beef chuck (3 lb.)
- Large onion (1 chopped)
- Carrots (1)

- Garlic (2 minced cloves)
- A-P flour (3 tbsp.)
- Beef broth (1.5 cups)
- Red wine (¼ of a bottle)
- Salt (1 tsp.)
- Black pepper (1 pinch)
- Rosemary (1 sprig)
- Thyme (2 sprigs)
- Bay leaf (1)
- Olive oil (2 tbsp.)
- White mushrooms (7-8 thick slices)
- Pearl onions (10 oz.)
- For the Garnish: Fresh parsley

Preparation Method:

1. Warm a dutch oven or other large pot to cook the diced bacon using the med-high temperature setting. When it's nicely browned, transfer it to a paper-lined platter using a slotted spoon. Save the diced bacon for breakfast or a dish of mashed potatoes or just trash it.
2. Slice the beef into two-inch portions and toss it into the pot to brown each side. Remove the meat from the pan.
3. Chop and mix in the onion to sauté until it's translucent (5 min.). Mince and add the garlic to sauté for about half a minute.
4. Add the beef back into the pot and dust it with three tablespoons of flour. Stir the meat until the flour has been absorbed (1 min.).
5. Add in the beef broth and just enough red wine to almost fully immerse it in juices. Stir and add a teaspoon of pepper and salt as

desired.

6. Tie the rosemary, thyme, and bay leaf together with a piece of kitchen twine, and drop the bouquet into the pot. Slice the carrots in half lengthwise, then cut into one-inch wide pieces, and add the carrots into the pot as well. Simmer them using the medium temperature setting. Cover the pot with a lid and adjust the temperature setting to med-low. Simmer the stew for about 2.2 to 3 hours until the beef is very tender.

7. Warm the olive oil in a large skillet using the med-low temperature setting. Add the sliced mushrooms and pearl onions, cooking until both are softened (7-8 min.). Set aside until ready to serve.

8. After the beef is ready, remove the herb packet.

9. Prepare a shallow bowl with the meat, sautéed mushrooms, pearl onions, and carrots. Add the sauce and garnish with a portion of chopped parsley.

Entrecote Steak With Red Wine Sauce

Servings Provided: 2

Time Required: 16 minutes

What is Needed:

- Rib-eye steaks (2 small)
- Black pepper & salt (as desired)
- Butter - unsalted (3 tbsp.)
- Shallot (1)
- Red wine (3 tbsp.)

- Beef stock (1/3 cup + 1 tbsp.)
- To Garnish: freshly chopped parsley

Preparation Method:

1. Generously sprinkle the steaks with pepper and salt.
2. Warm a cast-iron skillet using the high-temperature setting until it's 'smoking' hot. Add 1.5 tablespoons of butter to the pan, adjusting the setting to med-high.
3. Add the steaks to the hot buttered pan to cook for three minutes per side (medium doneness). Transfer the steaks to a platter for now.
4. Finely chop and add the shallot to the pan and sauté them for about a minute. Add the wine, and scrape the tasty browned bits with the juices from the bottom of the pan.
5. Reduce the temperature setting to medium, and stir in the beef stock. Simmer the mixture until the liquid has reduced by about half. Stir in the rest of the butter and prepare to serve it.
6. Use a sharp knife to slice the steaks at an angle and add the sauce. Garnish with a portion of fresh parsley.
7. Serve with your favorite side dish (ex. mashed potatoes, veggies, or french fries).

Pan-Seared Steak au Poivre

Servings Provided: 4

Time Required: 30 minutes

What is Needed:

- Filet mignons (4 small 1-inch each)
- Black peppercorns - cracked (1 tbsp.)
- Beef broth (.5 cup)
- Olive oil (1 tbsp.)
- Optional: Cognac (.25 cup)
- Cubed butter (2 tbsp.)

Preparation Method:

1. Use a paper towel to pat dry each filet and dust with pepper.
2. Warm a heavy cast-iron skillet using the medium-high heat until it's 'smoking' hot.
3. Flip the steaks and cook until small drops of red juice come to the surface (5 min. for medium). Transfer to a platter and keep them warm until time to add them to the mixture.
4. Empty the broth into the skillet to heat using the high-temperature setting and scrape up any browned bits.
5. At this point, add in the cognac and boil for one to two minutes to burn off the alcohol.
6. Remove the skillet from the burner. Whisk in the butter one cube at a time until melted.
7. Pour the sauce over the steaks and serve.

Steak Diane

Servings Provided: 2

Time Required: 30 minutes

What is Needed:

- Jus De Veau Lie/Veal Demi-Glace-Pwd FD (.5 cup)
- Dijon Mustard NB (1 tbsp.)
- Worcestershire Sauce (2 tsp.)
- Tomato paste - salt added (1 tsp. - canned)
- Spices - pepper, red or cayenne (1 pinch)
  The Steaks:

- Soybean oil (2 tsp.)

- Beef tenderloin (2 - 8 oz. trimmed to ¼- inch thickness)

- Black pepper & kosher salt (as desired)

- Butter - no-salt (1 tbsp.)

- Shallots (3 tbsp.)

- Cognac (.25 cup)

- Heavy whipping cream (.25 cup)

- Chives (2 tsp.)

Preparation Method:

1. Generously sprinkle the steaks with salt. Wait for them to reach room temperature while you make the sauce.

2. Use the high-temperature setting to warm the oil. Once it reaches a smoking point, add the steaks, and dot them with a few chunks of butter.

3. Sear the meat (high temp) until brown on each side, two to three minutes on each side, keeping them on the rare side (internal temp of 125° Fahrenheit. Transfer steaks to a warm plate.

4. Toss the shallots into the skillet and sauté them until softened (2-3 min.).

5. Remove the skillet to a cool burner and add in the Cognac. Carefully ignite it using a fireplace lighter. After the alcohol burns off and the flames go out, return the skillet to the high setting and wait for it to boil. Simmer for a few minutes to reduce its volume slightly.

6. Add demi-glace mixture, cream, and any accumulated juices from the steak. Cook on high heat just until the sauce starts to thicken (3-5 min.).

7. Transfer the steaks back into the pan and adjust the temperature setting

to low. Gently simmer until meat is heated through and cooked to your desired level of doneness.

8. Serve on a heated plate with a generous portion of sauce. Sprinkle with chives to your liking and serve.

Chapter 5: Other Delicious French Classics

French Ham & Grilled Cheese Sandwich - Croque Monsieur

Servings Provided: 4

Time Required: 25 minutes

What is Needed:

- Sourdough toast (8 slices)
- Gruyere cheese (8 oz.)
- Black forest ham (8 slices)
- Bechamel sauce (1 recipe)
- Dijon mustard
  The Sauce:

- Whole milk (1 cup)
- Unsalted butter (1 tbsp.)
- A-P flour (2 tbsp.)
- Pepper and salt (to your liking)

Preparation Method:

1. Make the sauce by warming the milk in a small saucepan using the med-low temperature setting until steam rises from the milk, but it has yet to boil. *Don't boil.*

2. Use another saucepan to melt the butter. Sift in the flour to create a bubbly, paste-like mixture. Slowly pour in hot milk, whisking it with a pinch of salt and pepper to your liking.

3. Stir the bechamel sauce using the low-temperature setting until it's thick enough to coat the back of a wooden spoon.

4. Set the oven using the broil function. Toast the bread slices and spread them with the mustard over half of the bread.

5. Prepare the sandwich using two slices of ham and shredded cheese on each. Top it using the ham with more shredded cheese.

6. Put the remaining bread slices over the ham and cheese to assemble the sandwiches. Spread about one to two tablespoons of bechamel sauce over the top of each sandwich. Sprinkle more shredded cheese on top of the bechamel.

7. Place the sandwiches on a baking tray and place the pan on the center oven rack until the cheese starts to melt.

8. Move the sandwiches to the top rack for about 30 seconds, removing when the cheese starts to obtain little golden spots.

Pork Chops With Mustard Sauce

Servings Provided: 4

Time Required: 20 minutes

What is Needed:

- Olive oil (3 tbsp.)
- Boneless pork chops (4 - 1-inch or 1.5 lb.)
- Black pepper & kosher salt (.5 tsp. each/as desired)
- Finely chopped shallots (2)
- Dry white wine (.75 cup)
- Heavy cream (2 tbsp.)
- Dijon mustard (1 tbsp.)
- Freshly chopped tarragon (1 tbsp.)
- Torn frisée pieces (1 small head/4 cups)
- Lemon wedges (1)

Preparation Method:

1. Heat oven to 400° Fahrenheit.
2. Warm one tablespoon of the oil in a large skillet using the medium-high temperature setting.
3. Sprinkle the pork using pepper and salt. Let them cook and brown for two to three minutes per side.
4. Transfer the pork to a baking tray and roast until thoroughly cooked (5-7 min.).
5. Meanwhile, add the shallots and one tablespoon of the oil to the skillet and cook, often stirring, until softened (3-4 min.)
6. Add the wine to the skillet and simmer until reduced by half. Add the cream and simmer until the sauce just thickens. Stir in the mustard.
7. Top the pork with the sauce and tarragon. Drizzle the frisée with the remaining tablespoon of oil and serve with the lemon wedges.

Provencal Chicken Casserole

Servings Provided: 4

Time Required: 53 minutes

What is Needed:

- Olive oil (5 tbsp.)
- Chicken - broilers/fryers/breast - meat only (4 @ 6 oz.)
- Lemon juice (1 lemon)
- Table salt (1 pinch)
- Cherry tomatoes (1.5 cups)
- Onions - Spring/scallions - include tops & bulb (1 bunch)
- Swanson Clear Chicken Broth CAM (.5 cup)
- Brown mustard - prepared (2 tbsp.)
- Fresh rosemary (1.5 sprigs)
- Fresh thyme (half bunch)
- Cheese - gruyere (2 cups)

Preparation Method:

1. Pour three tablespoons of olive oil into a shallow platter and lay chicken breasts on top. Rub with lemon juice, salt, and pepper.
2. Warm two tablespoons of olive oil in a nonstick skillet using the med-high temperature function. Cook the chicken breasts until browned (4 min. per side).
3. Preheat the oven at 350° Fahrenheit. Grease a baking dish. Place

tomatoes and green onions in the baking dish and pour the chicken broth on top.

4. Whisk the mustard, rosemary, and thyme in a small bowl and brush onto chicken breasts. Arrange the chicken breasts on top of the vegetables in the baking dish. Cover with the Gruyere cheese.

5. Bake the casserole on the middle rack until the chicken juices run clear and are no longer pink in the center (30 min.). (You can test it using an instant-read thermometer inserted into the center for a reading of at least 165° Fahrenheit.)

White Wine Coq Au Vin

Servings Provided: 6

Time Required: 55 minutes

What is Needed:

- Chicken - thighs, breasts & drumsticks (8 pieces/3 lb.)
- Black pepper & kosher salt
- Unsalted butter (2 tbsp.)
- Sliced bacon (4 diced)
- Large sweet onion (1)
- Garlic (3 minced cloves)
- Cremini mushrooms (1 pint - sliced)
- Dry white wine (2 cups)
- Whole-grain mustard (1 tbsp.)
- Heavy cream (.5 cup)

- Freshly chopped parsley (.25 cup)

Preparation Method:

1. Season the chicken with pepper and salt. Melt the butter in a large skillet using the medium temperature setting.
2. Arrange the chicken in the skillet and cook until it's well browned (4 min. per side).
3. Transfer the chicken from the skillet and set it aside. Add the bacon to the skillet and cook until the fat begins to render (3 min.).
4. Dice and mix in the onion and sauté until it is translucent (5 min.). Add the garlic and mushrooms, and sauté until the mushrooms are tender (5-6 min.).
5. Add the browned chicken back to the skillet. Pour the wine into the skillet, stir in the mustard, and bring the mixture to a simmer using the med-low temperature function. Cover the skillet and simmer until the chicken is almost fully cooked (15-20 min.).
6. Uncover the skillet and add the cream. Simmer until the sauce thickens and the chicken is fully cooked (8-10 min.).
7. Garnish with parsley and serve immediately.

PART V

Before we get started on your new recipes, let's learn how to make a delicious rub for your favorite meat.

Grilling Rub

What is Needed:

- Finely ground dark-roast coffee (3 tbsp.)
- Chili powder (3 tbsp.)
- Chipotle powder (1 tsp.)
- Dark brown sugar (3 tbsp.)
- Kosher salt (2 tbsp.)
- Smoked paprika (2 tbsp.)

- Dried thyme (1 tbsp.)

- Granulated garlic (1 tbsp.)

- Ground cumin (2 tsp.)

Preparation Method:

1. Be sure to pack the sugar when it's measured - tightly. Combine each of the fixings and rub them into the chosen meat.
2. Leave the rub on the meat for 12-24 hours before grilling.

Chapter 1: Seafood

Lemony Shrimp & Tomatoes

Servings Provided: 4 kabobs with ½ cup sauce each

Time Required: 25 minutes

What is Needed:

- Olive oil (2 tbsp.)
- Lemon juice (.33 cup)
- Grated lemon zest (.5 tsp.)
- Uncooked jumbo shrimp (1 lb.)
- Fresh arugula (2/3 cup)

- Sliced green onions (2)
- Plain yogurt (.25 cup)
- 2% milk (2 tsp.)
- Cider vinegar (1 tsp.)
- Sugar (.5 tsp.)
- Garlic (2 cloves)
- Dijon mustard (1 tsp.)
- Salt (.5 tsp. divided)
- Cherry tomatoes (12)
- Pepper (.25 tsp.)
- Also Needed: Skewers (4)

Preparation Method:

1. If you plan to use wooden skewers, be sure to soak them in water before you thread them.
2. Prepare a large mixing container and add the lemon juice, oil, minced garlic, and lemon zest, whisking until blended.
3. Fold in the shrimp and wait for about ten minutes.
4. Rinse and toss the arugula, green onions, yogurt, milk, vinegar, mustard, sugar, and ¼ of teaspoon salt in a food processor, pulsing until smooth.
5. Peel and devein the shrimp.
6. Prepare the skewers by alternating using the shrimp and tomatoes. Sprinkle it with pepper and rest of the salt.
7. Grill, covered, using the med-high temperature setting for two to three minutes per side or until shrimp are no longer pink.
8. Serve the kabobs with sauce.

Sea Bass With Garlic Butter

Servings Provided: 4

Time Required: 25 minutes

What is Needed:

- Sea bass (2 lb.)
- Butter (3 tbsp.)
- Lemon juice (1 medium lemon)
- Italian parsley (2 tbsp.)
- Olive oil (1.5 tbsp.)
- Cloves of garlic (2)

  Spices - .25 tsp. each:

- Garlic powder
- Paprika
- Onion powder
- Sea salt

Preparation Method:

1. Mince the garlic and finely chop the parsley.
2. Make the sauce. Prepare a saucepan to melt the butter and combine it with the lemon juice, garlic, and parsley. Transfer the pan to a cool burner once the butter has melted.
3. Warm the grill using the med-high temperature setting.

4. Oil the grates right before placing the fish onto the grill.

5. Combine the garlic, onion powder, paprika, pepper, and salt in a small mixing bowl.

6. Sprinkle the seasoning mixture on each side of the fish.

7. Grill the sea bass for seven minutes. Turn the fish and coat it with the butter sauce. Grill it for about seven additional minutes.

8. Once the fish reaches an internal temperature of at least 145° Fahrenheit, remove it from the heat, and spritz it with olive oil.

9. Serve it with your favorite sides.

Chapter 2: Pork

Grilled Sausages With Summer Veggies

Servings Provided: 12

Time Required: 60 minutes

What is Needed:

- Peach preserves (.75 cup)
- Soy sauce (.5 cup)
- Freshly minced ginger root (.5 cup)
- Water (3 tbsp.)
- Garlic (3 minced cloves)

- Optional: Hot pepper sauce (1 dash)
- Sweet red peppers (4 medium)
- Zucchini (3 small)
- Eggplant (1 medium)
- Yellow summer squash (2 small)
- Italian pork/turkey sausage links (12 hot @ 4 oz. each)

Preparation Method:

1. Measure and add the first five ingredients (up to the line) in a blender, adding the pepper sauce as desired. Cover with the lid and mix until blended.

2. Slice the zucchini and yellow squash lengthwise into quarters. Slice the peppers lengthwise in half and remove the seeds. Cut eggplant lengthwise into 1/2-inch-thick slices. Place all vegetables in a big mixing container and drizzle them using ½ cup of the sauce and toss to coat.

3. Place the veggies onto a greased grill rack. Grill, covered using medium heat until tender and lightly charred, turning once (8-10 min.). Cool slightly and adjust the grill temperature to the med-low setting.

4. Cut vegetables into bite-sized pieces. Toss with an additional ¼ cup sauce and keep warm.

5. Grill the sausages, covered, on med-low heat setting for 15-20 minutes or until a thermometer reads 160° Fahrenheit for pork sausages (165° Fahrenheit for turkey sausages) - turning occasionally. Remove sausages from grill and toss with the remaining sauce. Serve with vegetables.

Honey-Chipotle Ribs

Servings Provided: 12

Time Required: 1 hour 35 minutes

What is Needed:

- Pork baby back ribs (6 lb.)

  The Sauce:

- Ground chipotle pepper (4 tsp.)

- Chipotle peppers - in adobo sauce (2 tbsp.)

- Guinness beer (2 bottles - 11.2 oz ea.)

- Ketchup (3 cups)

- BBQ sauce (2 cups)

- Honey (2/3 cup)

- Onion (1 small)

- Worcestershire sauce (.25 cup)

- Dijon mustard (2 tbsp.)

- Black pepper (.5 tsp.)

- Salt (1 tsp.)

- Garlic powder (1 tsp.)

Preparation Method:

1. Chop the onion and chipotle peppers.
2. Wrap the ribs in large pieces of heavy-duty foil, sealing the edges of foil.
3. Grill the ribs with the lid 'on' while using indirect medium heat until tender (1-1.5 hrs.).
4. Combine the sauce ingredients in a large saucepan.
5. Adjust the temperature setting to simmer, uncovered, for about 45 minutes - until thickened - stirring occasionally.
6. Remove ribs from foil and place over direct heat. Baste them with some of the sauce.
7. Grill the ribs with the lid on, using the medium temperature setting for about half an hour or until browned, turning once and occasionally basting with additional sauce.
8. Serve with the rest of the sauce.

Peachy Pork Ribs

Servings Provided: 4

Time Required: 2.5 hours

What is Needed:

- Pork baby back ribs (4 lb./in serving-sized portions)

- Water (.5 cup)

- Ripe peaches (3 medium)

- Onion (2 tbsp.)

- Butter (2 tbsp.)

- Garlic (1 clove)

- Lemon juice (3 tbsp.)

- Orange juice concentrate (2 tbsp.)

- Soy sauce (2 tsp.)

- Ground mustard (.5 tsp.)

- Brown sugar (1 tbsp.)

- Salt (.25 tsp.)

Preparation Method:

1. Mince the garlic and onion.
2. Add the ribs into a shallow roasting pan of water.
3. Place a layer of foil over the pan, and bake at 325° Fahrenheit for two hours.
4. Peel and cube the peaches and toss them into a blender, cover, and process until blended.
5. Prepare a small saucepan to melt the butter. Sauté the onion until tender. Mix in the garlic and sauté for one more minute. Stir in the lemon juice, orange juice concentrate, soy sauce, brown sugar, mustard, pepper, salt, and pureed peaches. Warm until thoroughly heated.
6. Drain the ribs. Spoon some of the sauce over ribs.
7. Grill the ribs using the medium temperature setting on a lightly oiled rack, covered, for eight to ten minutes or until browned, turning occasionally and brushing with sauce.

Pork Loin Steaks

Servings Provided: 2

Time Required: 25 minutes

What is Needed:

- Pork loin steaks (4 boneless)
- Water (.25 cup)
- Dried oregano (1 tsp.)
- Brown sugar (2 tbsp.)

Preparation Method:

1. Use a non-metallic container to combine the marinade fixings.
2. Add the steaks to the bowl and cover to marinate overnight or for a minimum of two hours in the fridge.
3. Prepare the grill using the med-high temperature setting.
4. Grill the steaks for three to five minutes on each side and serve with your favorite side dishes.

Chapter 3: Poultry

Chicago-Style Turkey Dogs

Servings Provided: 4

Time Required: 20 minutes

What is Needed:

- Turkey hot dogs (4)
- Whole wheat tortillas (4 @ 8-inch - warmed)
- Sandwich pickle slices (4 thin)
- Chopped sweet onions (.5 cup)
- Optional Toppings:
- Prepared mustard
- Pickled hot peppers
- Cheddar cheese

Preparation Method:

1. Grill the hot dogs until they are as you like them - with the grill marks.
2. Serve in a tortilla with a portion of tomatoes, cucumber, pickles, and onions.
3. Add more toppings as desired.

Dr. Pepper Drumsticks

Servings Provided: 6

Time Required: 50 minutes

What is Needed:

- Dr. Pepper (2/3 cup)
- Ketchup (1 cup)
- Bourbon (2 tbsp.)
- Brown sugar (2 tbsp.)
- Salt (.125 tsp.)
- BBQ seasoning (4 tsp.)
- Worcestershire sauce (1 tbsp.)
- Optional: Celery salt (.25 tsp.)

- Chicken drumsticks (12)

Preparation Method:

1. Combine the sauce fixings (up to the line) in a saucepan. Add the celery salt as desired. Wait for it to boil and adjust the temperature setting to simmer, uncovered, for eight to ten minutes or until slightly thickened, stirring often.
2. On an oiled grill using the med-low temperature setting, cook the chicken, covered for 15 minutes. Turn and continue to grill 15-20 minutes until an internal thermometer reads 170°-175° Fahrenheit. Brush it occasionally with sauce.
3.

Grilled Lemon Chicken

Servings Provided: 12

Time Required: 45 minutes

What is Needed:

- Fryer/broiler chickens - cut up (3-3.5 lb. each)
- Lemonade concentrate - thawed (.75 cup)
- Soy sauce (.33 cup)
- Garlic (1 clove)
- Seasoned salt (1 tsp.)
- Garlic powder (.125 tsp.)
- Celery salt (.5 tsp.)

Preparation Method:

1. Mince the garlic and mix all of the fixings except for the pieces of chicken.
2. Pour half of the mixture into a shallow glass dish. Use a layer of foil or plastic to cover the bowl and place the rest of the lemonade mixture in the fridge.
3. Dip the chicken into lemonade mixture, turning to coat and trash the used marinade.
4. Grill the chicken, covered, using the medium-temperature setting for 30 minutes, turning occasionally. Brush with the reserved lemonade mixture.
5. Grill it for another 10-20 minutes, frequently basting, until a thermometer reads 165° Fahrenheit.

Ground Turkey Burgers

Servings Provided: 6

Time Required: 30 minutes

What is Needed:

- Whisked egg (1 large)
- Whole wheat breadcrumbs (2/3 cup)
- Celery (.5 cup)
- Onion (.25 cup)
- Freshly minced parsley (1 tbsp.)
- Worcestershire sauce (1 tsp.)

- Pepper (.25 tsp)
- Salt (.5 tsp.)
- Dried oregano (1 tsp.)
- Lean ground turkey (1.25 lb.)
- Split whole wheat burger buns (6 whole)

Preparation Method:

1. Chop the onion and celery.
2. Combine the breadcrumbs, egg, celery, seasonings, onion, parsley, and Worcestershire sauce.
3. Add the turkey and shape into patties.
4. Prepare on the grill using the medium-temperature setting until they reach an internal temp of 165° Fahrenheit.
5. Serve the burgers on the buns as desired.

Spiced Chicken With Cilantro Lime Butter

Servings Provided: 6

Time Required: 55 minutes

What is Needed:

The Sauce Ingredients:

- Chili powder (1 tbsp.)
- Ground cinnamon (2 tsp.)
- Brown sugar (1 tbsp.)
- Baking cocoa (1 tsp.)
- Balsamic vinegar (1 tbsp.)
- Pepper & salt (.5 tsp. each)
- Olive oil (3 tbsp.)
- Bone-in breast halves (6 @ 8 oz. each)

The Lime Butter:

- Melted butter (.33 cup)
- Cilantro (.25 cup)
- Red onion (2 tbsp.)
- Serrano pepper (1)
- Black pepper (.125 tsp.)
- Lime juice (1 tbsp.)

Preparation Method:

1. Finely chop the cilantro, onion, and serrano pepper.
2. Combine the sauce fixings; brown sugar, chili powder, cinnamon, cocoa, pepper, salt, vinegar, and oil. Brush the mixture over chicken.
3. Arrange the chicken skin-side down on the grill rack.
4. Grill the chicken - covered for 15 minutes (indirect medium heat).
5. Flip it over and continue to grill for 20-25 minutes longer (internal temp of 165 °Fahrenheit.
6. Combine the butter fixings to drizzle over the chicken before serving.

Turkey Pepper Kabobs

Servings Provided: 4

Time Required: 25 minutes

What is Needed:

- Unsweetened pineapple chunks (8 oz. can)

- Brown sugar (.25 cup - packed)

- Worcestershire sauce (2 tbsp.)

- Canola oil (2 tbsp.)

- Garlic (1 clove)

- Prepared mustard (1 tsp.)

- Turkey breast tenderloins (1 lb.)

- Green pepper (1 large)

- Sweet onion (1 large - 0.75-inch pieces)

- Red sweet pepper (1 large)

Preparation Method:

1. Chop the turkey and sweet peppers into one-inch pieces.
2. Drain the pineapple, saving ¼ cup of the juice.
3. Prepare the marinade by mixing the brown sugar with the oil, mustard, Worcestershire sauce, minced garlic, and reserved juice.
4. In another mixing container, cube and toss in the turkey with 1/3 cup of marinade. Refrigerate it covered for two to three hours. Cover and refrigerate the rest of the marinade.
5. On eight soaked wooden skewers or metal, alternately thread the turkey, veggies, and pineapple chunks. Discard the remaining marinade.
6. Arrange the kabobs on an oiled grill rack using medium heat. Grill, covered, until the turkey is no longer pink (8-10 min.), turning occasionally
7. Note: Baste them frequently with the reserved marinade during the last three minutes.

Chapter 4: Beef

Classic Beef Cheeseburgers

Servings Provided: 4

Time Required: 30 minutes

What is Needed:

- 90% lean ground beef (1 lb.)
- Steak seasoning blend (1.5 tsp.)
- Burger buns (4 - split)
- American/Cheddar/Swiss cheese (4 slices)
- Lettuce (4 leaves)
- Tomato (4 slices)

Optional Toppings:

- Mustard
- Ketchup
- Onion slices
- Pickle slices

Preparation Method:

1. Prepare the grill until it reaches medium ash-covered coals.

2. While it heats, mix the beef and steak seasoning in a large mixing container, shaping it into four ½ -inch thick patties.

3. Arrange the patties on the grid over the coals. Grill the burgers covered for 8 to 10 minutes (for a gas grill 7-9 min.), occasionally turning until an instant-read thermometer inserted horizontally into its center registers at 160° Fahrenheit.

4. About two minutes before the burgers are done, arrange the buns, cut side down, on the grid. Grill until lightly toasted. During the last minute of grilling, top each burger with a slice of cheese to melt.

5. Line the bottom of each bun with lettuce, topping it with the burger, tomato, and chosen toppings. Close the sandwiches and serve.

Grilled Skirt Steak With Peppers & Onions

Servings Provided: 6

Time Required: 50 minutes

What is Needed:

- Apple juice (.5 cup)

- Red wine vinegar (.5 cup)

- Yellow/white onion (.25 cup)

- Rubbed sage (2 tbsp.)

- Ground mustard (3 tsp.)

- Salt (1 tsp.)

- Ground coriander (3 tsp.)

- Black pepper (3 tsp.)

- Garlic clove (1 minced)

- Olive oil (1 cup)

- Beef skirt steak (1.5 lb.)

- Red onions (2 medium)

- Sweet red peppers (2 medium)

- Green onions (12)

Preparation Method:

1. Finely chop the onion, slice the peppers into halves, and trim the green onions. Cut the steak into 5-inch pieces and slice the red onions into ½-in slices.

2. Whisk the first nine ingredients (up to the line) until blended.

3. Slowly whisk in oil. Pour 1.5 cups of the marinade into a large resealable plastic bag. Toss in the beef and seal the bag - tossing it to coat. Refrigerate it overnight. Also, cover and refrigerate the rest of the marinade.

4. Toss the rest of the veggies with ¼ cup of the reserved marinade. Grill the red onions and peppers, covered, using the medium temperature setting (4-6 min. per side)until tender. Grill the green onions one to two minutes until tender.

5. Drain the beef, and trash the marinade in the bag.

6. Grill the beef covered using medium heat (4-6 min. per side) until the meat reaches desired doneness (for medium-rare, a thermometer should read 135° Fahrenheit; medium, 140° Fahrenheit; medium-well, 145° Fahrenheit). Baste with the remaining marinade during the last four minutes of cooking. Let the steak stand for five minutes.

7. Chop the veggies into small pieces and transfer them into an over-sized mixing container. Slice the steak diagonally across the grain into thin slices, add to vegetables, and toss to combine.

8. Serve and enjoy it when it's ready.

Tangy Lime Top Round Steak

Servings Provided: 4

Time Required: 25 minutes

What is Needed:

- Top round steak (1 lb.)
- Fresh lime juice (.25 cup)
- Worcestershire sauce (1 tbsp.)
- Brown sugar - lightly packed (2 tbsp.)
- Vegetable oil (2 tbsp.)

- Garlic (1 tbsp. - minced)

Preparation Method:

1. Whisk the juice, sugar, oil, Worcestershire, and minced garlic in a small mixing container.
2. Trim the steak, slicing it to a ¾-inch thickness.
3. Place the steak and lime mixture in a zipper-type plastic bag; toss the steak to coat. Securely close the bag and marinate in the fridge for six hours or overnight - turning intermittently.
4. Trash the marinade and place the steak on the grill grid using medium ash-covered coals.
5. Grill, covered for 10-11 minutes, turning occasionally. Don't overcook it. (For medium-rare: 145° Fahrenheit internal temp.)
6. Carve the steak into thin slices.

Whiskey Cheddar Burgers

Servings Provided: 8

Time Required: 30 minutes

What is Needed:

- Whiskey (.25 cup)
- Soy sauce (1 tbsp.)
- Black pepper and salt (.5 tsp. each)
- Worcestershire sauce (1 tbsp.)

- Shredded sharp cheddar cheese (1 cup)

- Onion (.25 cup)

- Seasoned breadcrumbs (2 tbsp.)

- Cloves of garlic (3)

- Paprika (.5 tsp.)

- Dried basil (.5 tsp.)

- Lean ground beef (1.5 lb.)

- Onion/burger buns - split (8)

  Optional Toppings:

- Lettuce

- Sliced tomatoes

- BBQ sauce

- Cheddar cheese slices

Preparation Method:

1. Finely chop the onions and cloves. Combine all of the fixings, adding the beef, last.
2. Thoroughly, but gently, combine the mix shaping it into eight ½-inch-thick patties.
3. Prepare a greased grill, using the medium temperature setting.
4. Cook the burgers, covered, for four to five minutes on each side or until a thermometer reads 160° Fahrenheit (internally).
5. Serve the burgers on rolls with toppings as desired.

Chapter 5: Dessert

Grilled Pineapple With Lime Dip

Servings Provided: 8

Time Required: 30 minutes

What is Needed:

- Fresh pineapple (1)
- Lime juice (2 tbsp.)
- Packed brown sugar (.25 cup)
- Honey (3 tbsp.)
  The Dip:

- Grated lime zest (1 tsp.)
- Brown sugar (1 tbsp.)

- Lime juice (1 tbsp.)
- Honey (2 tbsp.)
- Unchilled cream cheese (3 oz.)
- Plain yogurt (.25 cup)

Preparation Method:

1. Spritz the grill rack using a cooking oil spray before warming the grill. Peel and core the pineapple and slice it vertically into eight wedges. Cut each wedge horizontally into two spears.

2. Combine the honey, brown sugar, and lime juice in a shallow dish and add the pineapple. Toss it and cover to refrigerate for one hour.

3. Beat cream cheese until smooth. Mix in the yogurt with the honey, brown sugar, lime juice, and zest. Cover and pop it into the fridge until it's time to serve.

4. Drain the pineapple, discarding marinade. Grill the pineapple spears using the medium temperature setting (lid on) for three to four minutes per side or until they have grill marks that are golden brown. Serve with the lime dip.

Take Care Of Your Grill!

How to Clean the Grill:

1. Gather a few folded paper towels. Use a large pair of tongs and a high smoke point oil (ex. peanut, sunflower, canola). Olive oil will work in a pinch.

2. Dip the paper towels into a portion of the chosen oil and run it across the grates at least three times to create a non-stick surface to help prevent the meat or fish from breaking during the cooking process.

3. Easy - yet healthy!

9 781913 710668